Dive Sites & Marine Life of the Calf of Man
&
neighbouring area

BILL SANDERSON

BRUCE McGREGOR

ANDREW BRIERLEY

Production Director: Paula Casey-Vine
Design and setting: Shirley Kilpatrick (Icon)

A CIP catalogue record for this book is available from the British Library

ISBN 1-898162-80-8

Immel Publishing Ltd
20 Berkeley Street
Berkeley Square
London W1X 5AE

Telephone: 071 491 1799
Facsimile: 071 493 5524

Cover photograph by Bill Sanderson

Contents

Acknowledgements

WE would like to thank the numerous people and organisations who contributed toward the completion of this work.

Financial support for production and publication of the book came from the Esmée Fairbairn Charitable Trust with additional support from the Calf Marine Trust, Pacini Ltd, and the World Wide Fund For Nature in conjunction with National Westminster Bank.

Janette Allen kindly loaned her computer and heater for the final compilation stages. John Bishop, Stanley Clucas, Larch Garrad, Steve Hawkins, Debbie Jones, John Slinn, Jill Strawbridge, and Ken Watterson diligently read the manuscript providing many constructive suggestions which doubtless improved the final product.

Elaine Fisher and Chris Bridge provided two of the surface photographs, and Pacini Ltd, Ulric Wilson and John Moon provided facilities for aerial photography.

We would like to extend a special thanks to Mike Bates, whose twenty five years of local diving experience, and ceaseless efforts to promote marine conservation, have enabled him to provide a unique and invaluable contribution.

Debbie and Cayt deserve a very special thank you for their unerring patience and support throughout.

Finally, to all our long suffering friends and colleagues who have cheerfully dived with us in rain or shine, winter or summer, come hell or high water over the past six years, and made researching this book a truly enjoyable labour of love, thank you!

About the Book

BORN of more than a thousand dives around the coast of the Calf of Man, this book paints an inspiring picture of an extremely beautiful area of the Manx coastline, promoting diving and conservation in this prolific marine environment.

The book begins with an account of the rich and varied history of the Calf of Man. The other introductory chapters provide a valuable insight into marine biology and a discussion of conservation attitudes, as well as giving general diving information about this exceptional area.

The book goes on to describe a selection of outstanding dive sites in the south of the Isle of Man, most of which are around the Calf. Also included are several excellent dives on the way to the Calf from the two most usual launch sites, Port Erin and Port St Mary.

The Calf and its surroundings provide enormous variety and numerous challenges to the diver, including drift diving, sensational scenic diving, wreck diving, cave diving and intriguing night dive sites. Although great experience is required for a few of the sites described, there is something here for everyone. Some of the more adventurous sites can in fact still be tackled by the less experienced diver when there are good slack and surface conditions on neap tides. Drift dives, allowing one to get the most out of the varying scenery and marine life present, are described in some instances. At other locations however, it is inadvisable to dive except at slack water. This and other detailed information is provided for each dive site in the section 'Dive Site Details', and is accompanied by a photograph, often aerial, of the location, which aids interpretation of the maps.

The maps of the dive sites show depths in metres and underwater features such as gullies and cliffs, as well as specific points of interest such as good entry locations for divers. The general key shown here applies to all the maps.

In the 'General Description and Biology' section a description of a selection of the marine life likely to be encountered at each site are given. This section gives observations and general points of interest about these various organisms but is not intended to be a laborious, categoric species list. Such information is readily available elsewhere, and the keener marine enthusiast can find further details in the guides and texts listed in the Bibliography.

General Key:

	Land
	Intertidal
	Building
	Lighthouse/light
	Wreck visible at low tide
Ⓐ *	Symbols referred to in text
20	Approximate depth in metres

Dive Sites and Marine Life of the Calf of Man represents the culmination of considerable diving experience combined with an understanding of the marine life around the Calf of Man and surrounding areas. It aims to kindle interest in the special submarine world on our doorstep, and to provide more for the inquisitive diver than just the logistics of going for a dive.

Although every effort has been made to ensure the accuracy of information contained in this book, the authors can take no responsibility for dives carried out under its guidance. Parameters such as slack water times are subject to variation at the hands of a number of factors including, not least, the changeable Manx weather, and consequently should be taken as best estimates only. Depths will of course vary with tidal state, values given are approximate and, although we consider them to be truly representative, they should not be used exclusively in planning dive profiles. As always divers are wholeheartedly encouraged to use their own judgement and common sense, and are urged to proceed with the degree of caution appropriate to this adventurous sport.

The Calf of Man

AT the extreme south-western tip of the Isle of Man lies a small, isolated island called the Calf of Man, which is steeped in history and legend. This small island, a little more than one and a half miles at its widest and with a total area of only 600 acres, has supported in its time the world's largest known population of Manx shearwaters (*Puffinus puffinus*); a population of over thirty farm workers; various hermits; lighthouse keepers; shipwrecked sailors; mythical pirates; a monk; and a mischievous collection of fairies!

This cliff strewn, secluded piece of Manx coastline is presently owned by Manx National Heritage and occupied by no more than a handful of lighthouse keepers and a seasonal nature reserve warden and assistant. This calm current state of affairs however belies the islet's colourful past.

The first presumed owner of the Calf was the Viking chief Godred Crovan I back in 1079. The records only become clear, however, when Sir John Stanley, then Lord of Mann, came into control and sold the island to the old Manx family of Stevenson. This event is chronicled in the Manorial Roll of 1511. During the next century, the Calf became the possession of successive generations of Earls of Derby, except for a brief spell when the seventh Earl picked the wrong side in the English Civil War, and lost the land to the Commonwealth and his head to the parliamentarians! The eighth Earl of Derby, however, regained possession of the islet in 1736. It then passed in the female line to the Duke of Athol's family and was subsequently handed down to the next generation. The subsequent owner was the English Crown, who immediately sold it to the wealthy Drinkwater family. From 1830 to 1937 the Calf passed through the hands of three more wealthy families, who let the islet as farm land. A chance encounter on a train between a Mr J. Appleyard Popplewell, then proprietor, and a Mr F. J. Dickens, a distant relative of the

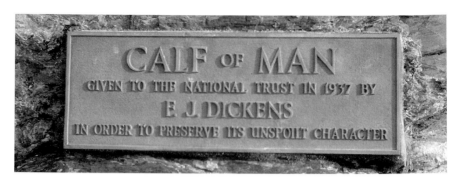

Plaque at Cow harbour, Calf of Man.

famous author Charles, resulted in a deal whereby the island was purchased and donated to the English National Trust. The final transaction, which saw the islet further donated to what is now known as Manx National Heritage, has secured the peaceful solitude and rugged natural beauty of the islet, making it available for the inspiration and enjoyment of many future generations of nature lovers.

This small piece of Manx heritage is also part of an international network of bird observatories, and is of great value since the island is on an important migration route. Birds ringed on the Calf have been discovered as far away as North Africa. It is estimated that there have now been over 140,000 birds ringed, about 140 species recorded visiting the island and more than 30 species recorded as nesting there.

The Calf, or Kalfr as it was known to the Norse, has over the years been the centre of a good deal of hunting and farming activity. Legend has it that it was whilst he was on a deer stalking expedition to the Calf that the local Manx people conspired against the ruthless Viking Chief Kitter. It was feared that since he had obliterated the game in the south of the Isle of Man, and had consequently resorted to arduous excursions in order to satiate his blood lust, he would soon be after the local cows! In desperate haste to return to his mysteriously blazing house at South Barrule, the less than popular Chief and his henchmen foolishly hurried across the dangerous Calf Sound, whilst it was in full flood, in their state-of-the-art coracle. Not surprisingly they were lost in the flow around Kitterland, a small rocky islet that bears his name to this day.

It is, however, not for its deer that the Calf is well known. In fact, over the years several vain attempts have been made to establish them here. Possibly the most desired game in these parts was the Manx shearwater, of which the Calf may once have boasted the world's largest colony, supporting an annual harvest of around 10,000 birds. These birds were taken young and considered something of a delicacy, with a taste likened to caviar. They were often exported salted or in brine. The birds disappeared entirely from this, their Manx home, very shortly after a shipping disaster in 1786. The problem, apart from the demise of the crew, was the escape of *Rattus norvegicus* from this 700-ton shipwreck (it is considered exceedingly bad luck to utter the common English name for this domestic rodent on the Isle of Man, hence we use the Manx euphemism, longtail). The longtails were not indigenous to the Calf and bred well, apparently feeding on the eggs and young birds from their nests in small hollows or rabbit burrows. Sadly, despite persistent attempts to eradicate the longtail population, the Manx shearwater did not breed on the Calf for about 180 years. However, a handful of recent sightings give hope that there is possibly a tiny recovery under way.

There has been a multitude of shipping disasters around the Calf and it is possible to identify well over a hundred incidents, many being a result of tremendous storms during the pre-lighthouse era. One persistently occurring force in these disasters has been the treacherous Calf Sound, which has held many a vessel in its vicious tidal grip and dashed them on to the rocks. Throughout history this tidal factor has repeatedly been compounded by heavy fog conditions. Vessels such as the *Clan Mc Master* in 1923 and the *St Ronan* in 1958, believing themselves to be well clear of the Calf, ordered 'dead slow' in fog, and in so doing surrendered themselves to the mercy of the Sound.

On Boxing Day in 1852 an incredible and tragic wrecking occurred in the Sound. The 169 ton brigantine *Lily* was smashed up on Kitterland during a fearful storm with the loss of many of her crew. The real disaster happened the next day however when the Lloyds sub-agent came to inspect the damage. Unbeknown to the crowd of spectators, a group of lads had been aboard the night before, pilfering from the wreck, and had left a candle burning. A fire had smouldered overnight amongst the cotton goods in the ship's cargo and, when smoke was seen emerging from one of the hatches, a great team of fire fighting volunteers was assembled. No sooner had the deck planks been torn open than fire flared in the hold, igniting 61 tonnes of gunpowder amongst the cargo. The blast left pieces of the wreck strewn as far away as Castletown, caused miners at Ballacorkish Mine to drop their tools in a state of panic, left 22 widows, 74 orphans and hardly any trace of the 29 bodies. The devastated community of Port St Mary was only able to bury three coffins for all the men lost, and the Reverend Gregory Page was moved to compile a detailed poem chronicling the disaster, within which he sympathised with the bereaved:

> But they alone the dreadful bolt will feel,
> Whose house is smitten and their kindred slain,
> And in who's home, fire, death, and ruin reign...

A recently restored memorial in Rushen churchyard bears testament to this disaster.

The Thousla cross near the Calf Sound Café is a monument to another loss in these treacherous seas, that of the French ship *Jeanne St Charles*, only six years later. The Thousla Rock mark was erected in the wake of this saga to try and curb such grizzly incidents.

In 1833 the *Manx Sun* newspaper advertised the first known ferry service to the Calf, heralding the arrival of tourism to this secluded islet. Despite the ominous maritime reputation and the number of victims claimed both in legend and reality, the Calf of Man, with its craggy natural beauty and wildlife, can be safely visited by sightseers aboard charter boats from Port Erin and Port St Mary, and is now a regular stop-off point for dive boats and other pleasure craft.

This mystical, wondrous and historic place is thoroughly recommended to any visitor, be they diver, ornithologist or anyone with a general appreciation of wild beauty. For the diver, there is the added delight of having the privilege of exploring a superb diversity of marine life amongst some of the best scenic diving to be found in the British Isles.

Diving the Calf

View looking south-west to the Calf of Man.

LAUNCH, LANDINGS AND LUNCH

THE isolated nature of the Calf of Man and the severity of tidal streams in the area necessitate diving from boats. Well kept public slipways are to be found in Port Erin close to Raglan Pier, and in Port St Mary between the Albert Pier and the Lifeboat House, as shown in the site maps for Port Erin Bay (page 30) and the Port St Mary Ledges drift dive (page 82).

Both ports provide convenient departure points for dives around the Calf of Man and other sites in the vicinity. The positioning of these harbours, and the geography of the Calf itself, ensure that launching and diving will usually be possible somewhere under most wind directions.

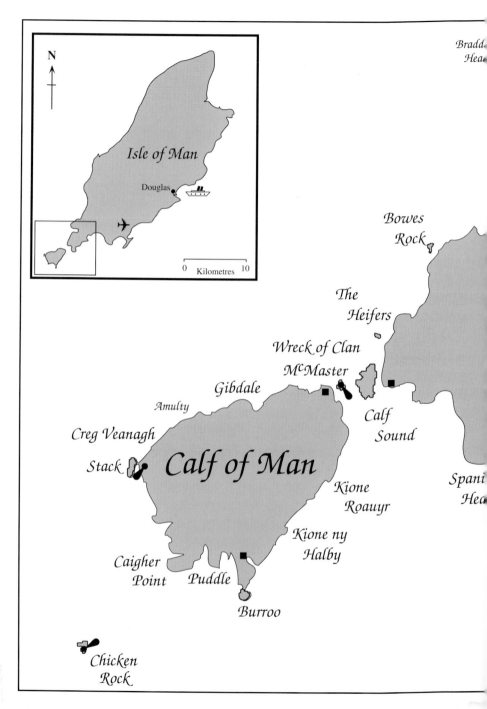

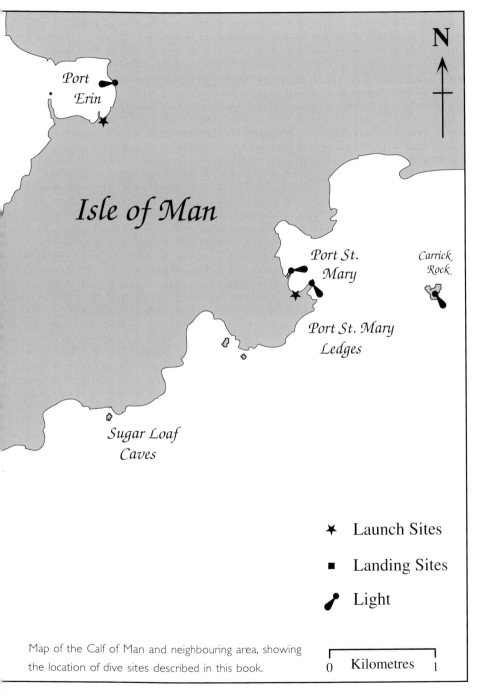

Port
Erin

N

Isle of Man

Port St.
Mary

Carrick
Rock

Port St. Mary
Ledges

Sugar Loaf
Caves

✶ Launch Sites

■ Landing Sites

🍆 Light

Map of the Calf of Man and neighbouring area, showing
the location of dive sites described in this book.

0   Kilometres   1

Visitors landing on the Calf are required by the Manx National Heritage to use the formal sites of Cow, Grant's (see map on page 44) or South Harbour (see map on page 66), and to keep to designated paths. It is, however, feasible to land on the Calf at many additional places in an emergency.

Passengers can be put ashore on the Isle of Man directly opposite the Calf across the Sound at Cabbyl Ghaw (see map on page 44). From here a few steps and a short walk lead to the Calf Sound Café, an unlikely-looking building which has withstood the elements at this exposed site for nearly a century. This establishment, which has recently turned the blustery environs to its advantage, as the wind turbine on the roof testifies, provides excellent food and refreshments. There is also a public toilet for the desperately dry-suited diver!

Port Erin and Port St Mary offer a number of convenient shorefront eating places, as well as a collection of pubs and shops. Both villages have chip-shops a short walk from the seafront.

TIDES

The Calf is swept at times by what can only be described as ferocious tidal currents. Generally speaking these currents follow the pattern in the diagrams below. The influence of these currents varies from site to site, and on a more localised basis within sites. They give rise to high energy environments in current exposed areas, as compared to low energy environments in more sheltered localities.

More detailed current information is given in each individual dive site section and in all cases is discussed with reference to high and low water at

Flood

Ebb

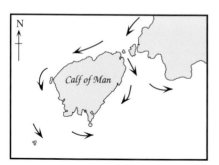
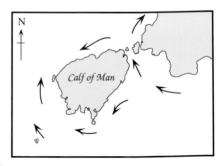

Liverpool. Copies of Liverpool tide tables are readily available from shops around the Island.

The profound influence which currents can have on the dive sites of the Calf and neighbouring area necessitate careful planning and consideration of the experience of members of the dive party. In all cases it is advisable to turn up early on the site to get the most out of the somewhat variable slack times.

MANX SPORT DIVING AMENITIES

Charter boat K.T.B., Port Erin	Tel. 0624 832339
Diving Air Services, Douglas	Tel. 0624 628123
BSAC Dive School, Port St Mary	Tel. 0624 832943
Aquatech Diving Services	Tel. 0624 833037

EMERGENCY

Divers visiting the Isle of Man will be reassured to know that the Island's capital, Douglas, is home to one of the most modern and sophisticated recompression facilities in the British Isles (tel. 0624 626394). Additionally, both Port Erin and Port St. Mary are home to lifeboats. Liverpool Coastguard, who can be contacted by dialling 999 or on VHF Channel 16, will co-ordinate these facilities in the event of an emergency. The knowledge that such excellent rescue facilities are close at hand should not, however, make divers any less cautious or well prepared.

Diving Towards Conservation

THE Calf of Man is without doubt a special place for marine life. Below the waves, beyond the view of many, its intricate rocky coastal topography extends into the alluring depths. This variable terrain, in conjunction with strong tidal forces, has created a myriad of different marine habitats around the mere five-mile coastline, and has resulted in a concentrated feast of life that is a microcosm of Manx marine life as a whole.

This pristine part of Manx coastal waters is so unique and attractive that it has become very highly regarded amongst all who dive here, including very experienced divers, marine biologists and underwater photographers. In order to ensure that the marine life of the Calf survives in its present state, many people would like to see the area become a marine nature reserve. Local clubs which frequently dive around the Calf have their own self-imposed codes of conduct relating to the area. Many people dive here on a 'look but don't touch' basis. Although some divers are susceptible to collecting dinner from time to time, this area is generally regarded as something to be left as it is for future generations. We actively encourage all divers to adopt this attitude. Given that the Calf and its neighbouring area has such a wealth and diversity of marine life, and is consequently an important natural biological source, it would be encouraging to think that, as divers, we could enjoy its splendours and yet leave it unchanged.

Although some organisms appear resilient, it is very important to take care not to put knees down on the encrusting marine life and not to kick carelessly with fins. Some organisms such as the ross coral (*Pentapora foliacea*) are easily destroyed in seconds but take many years to grow.

Birds nesting on cliffs, not surprisingly, take to the air when approached by boats, which are perceived as posing a potential threat. If frequently disturbed,

Diver observes a lobster
(*Homarus gammarus*)

birds may choose to nest and feed elsewhere in future. The same could be said for the seals which bask luxuriously on the rocks around the Calf. In order to avoid disturbance, boats travelling at high speeds should keep well clear of nesting and haul-out sites, and should avoid rafts of birds, particularly as these may include young fledglings as yet unable to fly. It is possible that as leisure use in these waters continues to increase, animals not given due consideration may well cease to frequent the area.

As the popularity of sport diving continues to expand rapidly, it would be truly rewarding to think of people using this book to explore the treasures of the Calf of Man, but doing so in a manner which ensures that in ten, twenty or a hundred years' time this magical place will still be there to see and enjoy in all its current glory.

Science Speak

LATIN is used as the international language of scientific classification, and throughout many identification guides the Latin name of an organism is quoted italicised and in brackets after the common English name. In spite of their sometimes daunting and unpronounceable nature, these Latin names are invaluable as they are international, and provide unambiguous identification the world over. Latin names are free from sometimes confusing colloquial or international language variations. The fish *Lophius piscatorius*, for example, is known in Manx as guilley pern, and elsewhere as the angler fish, frog fish, fishing frog or monkfish!

The paired Latin names assigned to an organism are analogous to a car's make and model. The affectionately known 'Moggy' for example could more precisely be called *Morris minor*.

In this book we have tried to use, where possible, both common and Latin names. Many of the less familiar marine animals, however, have no common name and in such cases the Latin name alone is used.

In addition daunting technical or unfamiliar terms are explained in the glossary.

The Marine Machine

Oceans and seas cover around 71 per cent of the Earth's surface. The coastal margin of this once remote, inaccessible and sometimes hostile realm is now increasingly probed by a growing body of adventurers who regularly explore this alien world of outlandish shapes and forms.

The aim of this chapter is to lead curious divers through some of the wheels and cogs that make this marine machine tick, and to familiarise them with some of the seemingly strange and bizarre life forms with which they may be confronted in this ecosystem. All too often a diver surfaces from this unfamiliar environment to ask 'What does it do for a living?', or even 'Is it an animal or a plant?'! This chapter will hopefully shed some light on these and other such questions.

Who's Who?

The world beneath the waves holds many surprises with regard to relationships between the animal groups found there. It seems hard to believe at first glance, for example, that barnacles are more closely akin to crabs than they are to limpets.

In order to understand fully the seemingly confusing classification of organisms it is important to bear in mind that a great deal of other information, in addition to external appearance and structure, has been considered during the classification process. Closely related organisms adopting different lifestyles often evolve to look strikingly different, their fundamental similarities becoming masked, as with barnacles and crabs.

Common marine invertebrates (animals without backbones), such as sponges and anemones, are generally far less familiar to divers than are vertebrates, such as fish. Sea squirts are thought to be the group which provides the evolutionary link between invertebrates and vertebrates. The larvae of these animals have a primitive backbone like structure. Animals with backbones like fish, in turn, lead to amphibians (e.g. frogs), reptiles (e.g. snakes) and mammals. So, next time you poke a little blob of jelly on the rock, remember you might have just poked a relative!

The simplified family tree in diagram 1 shows the relationships between the most obvious and easily distinguished invertebrate animal groups commonly seen whilst diving around the Calf of Man. The more closely linked groups in the diagram are more closely related.

THE LIVING WEB

The marine world, like any other, is a complex, interrelated environment in which one creature provides food for another, which then itself becomes food for others, and so on. These interactions are not simply enclosed beneath the waves, since the land based, or terrestrial, world is inextricably linked with that of the sea.

When describing the feeding interactions of organisms around us, biologists often talk of food chains. Individual organisms which make up the component links in such food chains are often intricately embroiled in a web of interrelationships. Many individuals have the potential to feed on, and in turn become food for, a number of different organisms.

Diagram 2 represents the marine ecosystem of the Calf of Man, the arrows schematically showing the flow of food energy through this food web. This diagram also clearly illustrates the interdependence of all organisms within the system, both above and below the waves.

THE TURNING WHEELS

The links within food webs interact rather like cogs within a machine, with food energy being conveyed from one component to another. The following section describes in more detail the flow of food energy between the plant and animal cogs which comprise this marine machine.

THE GREAT PROVIDER

All creatures require energy to live and function, and they obtain this from their food. Initially the fuel for life comes from the sun, the great provider, in the form of light energy. Plants harness solar energy and use it as the driving

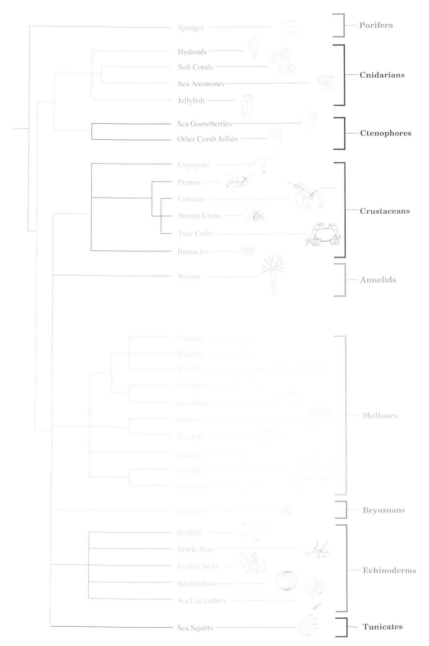

Diagram 1. Inter-relationships between some common invertebrate animal groups found whilst diving around the Calf of Man.

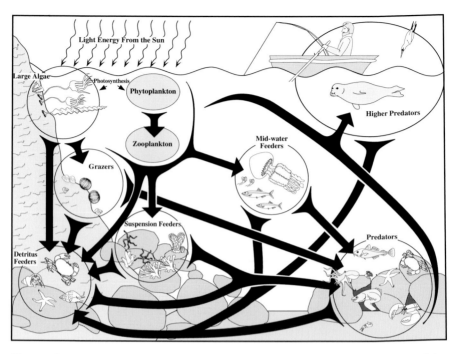

Diagram 2. A simplified food web, showing the flow of food energy between some of the major groups of organisms within the marine ecosystem of the Calf of Man. Each group, e.g. grazers, contains pictures of only a few representative organisms.

force to produce food, in the form of sugars, by a chemical process known as photosynthesis. Eighty per cent of all light entering the sea is absorbed in the first 10 metres of water. The majority of photosynthesis consequently occurs in this zone and most plant life is found here.

Diagram 3. Some common types of phytoplankton.

Around the Calf two broad categories of plants are at work. One comprises the large algae, or seaweeds, which are immediately obvious on the shores and in the shallow sea margins. The other type of plant is less conspicuous, but still of great importance, and comprises minute free-floating plants known collectively as phytoplankton. Diagram 3 shows some common types of phytoplankton, such as diatoms (D) and flagellates (Fl). Phytoplankton have the ability to reproduce by simply splitting in two, enabling their populations to multiply at staggering rates. Under favourable conditions some species, often red dinoflagellates, can become hyperabundant and create a visible mass called a red tide, which can be toxic in some cases.

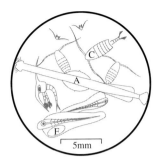

Diagram 4. Some common types of zooplankton.

Marine 'Sheep'

Grazing the phytoplankton soup are a host of small animals which live freely in the water column for some or all of their lives. A typical sample of these animals, known collectively as zooplankton and including copepods (C) and arrow worms (A), is illustrated in diagram 4. Of the 135,000 known invertebrate species which live on the sea bed, as many as 75 per cent have an initial planktonic larval phase. Many of these larvae are temporary grazers of phytoplankton, and join the great mass of herbivorous animals which spend their entire life in the water column.

Seaweeds also provide a direct food source for bottom dwelling grazers such as limpets, winkles, and topshells, which feed with a rasping belt of teeth. Known as a radula, this structure functions not unlike a belt sander! The familiar sea urchin (*Echinus esculentus*) has five flat teeth on its undersurface for grazing algae from underlying surfaces.

A Planktonic Feast

Planktonic animals and plants are consumed in part or indiscriminately by larger midwater grazers such as the herring (*Clupea harengus*). The basking shark (*Cetorhinus maximus*) strains planktonic food from the water with comb-like gill rakers. Planktonic predators include the gentle giant, non-stinging jellyfish, *Rhizostoma pulmo*, and the far smaller sea gooseberry (*Pleurobranchia pileus*) which trails strings of sticky fishing lines to catch its even smaller plankton prey.

More of the nutritious zooplankton and phytoplankton are devoured by an army of suspension feeding animals which live fixed to the sea bed. Sponges use thousands of small synchronously wiggling internal hair-cells to draw the food-rich water into their bodies through tiny surface pores. Similarly, bryozoans such as the hornwrack (*Flustra foliacea*), scallops (*Pecten maximus*), mussels

Basking shark (*Cetorhinus maximus*) feeding close to Chicken Rock during June 1990.

(*Mytilus edulis*) and sea squirts like *Ciona intestinalis* gently hoover up the sometimes bountiful supply. Wave-broken fragments from the larger seaweeds add to the particulate matter which suspension feeding organisms can feast upon.

Other predators like anemones and hydroids also live attached to the bottom. These wait with sticky stinging tentacles which immobilise and ensnare small zooplankton, or occasionally more sizeable prey items, as they pass by.

THE CHAIN CONTINUES

Energy for life progresses further along the chain, to the next level within the machine, as some of these grazing animals, planktonic and suspension feeders are themselves predated upon.

Shoaling herring (*Clupea harengus*) in Port Erin Bay.

Predatory fish, such as the cod (*Gadus morhua*) and wrasse species, selectively feed on shellfish, other smaller fish and crustaceans. The conger eel (*Conger conger*) on the other hand is reputed to feed on anything that moves!

More surprising, but no less voracious, predators are the tiny sea slugs or nudibranchs. These brightly coloured shell-less snails often feed on the seemingly impossible, such as hydroids which have batteries of defensive stinging cells. In an ironic twist the stinging cells from this quarry are ingeniously passed whole into the sea slug's own body and are then stored for its own defences!

The octopus (*Eledone cirrhosa*) is a vicious predator. Once its prey, often a crab, is ensnared amongst the web of legs, it is poisoned with neurotoxins and ripped apart by the octopus's powerful beak. The little cuttlefish (*Sepiola atlantica*), about four cm in length, is similarly equipped with a strong horny beak, although its prey is obviously much smaller and includes sand dwelling shrimps.

THE WASTE DISPOSERS

Eating can be a messy business but scraps from one man's table provide a feast elsewhere for others, with whole communities of detritovores existing on salvaging such waste. Everything in the food chain produces detritus (dead organic matter), be it dropped food, faeces, abraded plant material, particles of dead plankton, sloughed skin or whole carcasses.

The host of animals geared to eating this detrital matter, however, ensure that the energy it contains is not wasted. The common whelk or buckie (*Buccinum undatum*) is an avid detritovore and will eat just about anything, from silty remains to rotten carrion. Crabs are sometimes scavengers and have macerating mouth parts with which they grind up dead flesh.

Many bottom-dwelling suspension feeders ingest fine detrital particles in addition to living plankton and so can also be considered detritovores.

THE LIONS OF THE SEA

At the peak of the food chain are the more familiar but less numerous predators such as the grey seal (*Halichoerus grypus*), which eats a variety of fish species as well as some crabs. Birds, such as the gannet (*Sula bassana*) which can be seen dive-bombing the summer herring and mackerel shoals, are also amongst the higher predators.

A strangely familiar predator with no natural enemies also exists at the top of the food chain, one which has escaped the direct limitation on numbers usually imposed by the natural availability of food. This animal can modify the environment and exploit its food sources by sophisticated harvesting, fishing and agricultural techniques. This animal is of course man!

A CAUTIONARY TALE

Since all component organisms are inextricably linked through the food chain the effects of change on one part of the system will be transmitted from cog to cog, causing inevitable knock-on effects elsewhere in the machine. Oil spills, overfishing and general pollution for example, not only produce the immediately obvious mortalities, but often have other more subtle adverse effects. Overfishing not only results in diminished catches for the fishermen but also removes a food source for other predators such as seabirds. Pollution may result in the gradual debilitating accumulation of toxins in organisms which consume contaminated food.

All our actions have reactions within the finely balanced environment around us and great care is needed in order to preserve the marine machine, on which the whole world is dependent.

Dive Sites

Port Erin Bay

Port Erin Bay at low tide showing breakwater (left) and T-blocks (foreground).

DIVE SITE DETAILS

PORT Erin Bay is easily dived from the shore and offers numerous potential dives, several of which are presented here. The most popular sites in the bay are around the breakwater (A on map), the T-blocks (B) and the jetty (C).

The derelict breakwater, destroyed by a particularly violent storm in 1884, only eight years after its construction, runs roughly north from the entry steps (*). The T-blocks, the remains of the old quayside, run east from the same point towards the jetty. Access down the steps (*) for both the T-blocks and the breakwater becomes difficult at very low water as exposed and slippery

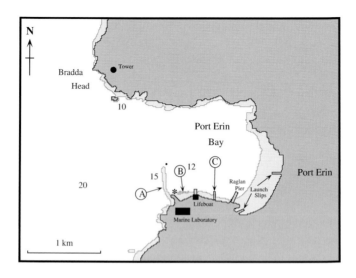

seaweed-covered boulders have to be negotiated. Inside the bay, the base of these ruins are on sand at around 10 to 12 m. It is possible to make an excursion over the top to the outside of the breakwater, to the sandy sea bed at around 15 m, except within approximately two hours of low water when the breakwater is exposed. The jetty (C) affords an easy dive of around six to eight metres, with a simple walk-in entry. It is also possible to follow the underwater boulder slope along the south of Port Erin Bay, past the lifeboat slip, between the T-blocks and the jetty.

Port Erin jetty, the inside of the old breakwater and the T-blocks are generally unaffected by tidal streams. There is, however, a 60-km fetch across the Irish Sea from the occasionally visible Mountains of Mourne on the east coast of Northern Ireland. Consequently, prevailing winds can occasionally cause the area to be quite rough making exit up the steps (*) tricky. There is, however, some shelter from wind and swells when the derelict breakwater is uncovered between mid and low water.

The breakwater is the site of an underwater nature trail constructed by Mike Bates, the chief diver at the Marine Laboratory which overlooks the bay. Port Erin Bay is also, from time to time, the site of underwater ecological experiments carried out by scientists from the Marine Laboratory, who would appreciate their sometimes bizarre-looking apparatus being left unmolested.

In many conditions Port Erin Bay is an easy and rewarding place to dive, both by day and night. Currents are not a worry and the area is easily dived without having to launch a boat. The bay offers a convenient second dive, is an excellent site for the less experienced diver, and is admirably suited for training exercises.

GENERAL DESCRIPTION AND BIOLOGY

Fish life often abounds here, with inquisitive ballan, corkwing and cuckoo wrasse (*Labrus bergylta, Crenilabrus melops* and *Labrus mixtus*) circling the diver in anticipation of an offered morsel. These fish can seem quite fearless and will sometimes swim close by. Incredibly, many wrasse start life as females, but after several years some become males. Most of the large ballan wrasse seen here are males and can be as old as 25. Occasionally pollack (*Pollachius pollachius*) are seen lingering warily in the distance. Coppery-coloured pouting or bib (*Trisopterus luscus*) shelter in small shoals amongst the concrete T-blocks, feeding on tiny fish, shrimps and shellfish. Comic-faced tompot and Yarrell's blennies (*Parablennius gattorugine* and *Chirolophis ascanii*) can occasionally be found on and around the jetty, as well as scorpion fish (*Taurulus bubalis*), which are heavily armoured with bony plates. The gorgeous pale blue of the leopard spotted goby (*Thorogobius ephippiatus*) can be seen in rocky recesses. Two spot gobies (*Gobiusculus flavescens*) and small shoals of larval fish can also be encountered around the weed and rocks.

An abundant army of grazing edible sea urchins (*Echinus esculentus*) roam throughout, their ranks massed in the deeper zone below the kelp forested upper ramparts of the ruined sea defences.

Off on the sand, plaice (*Pleuronectes platessa*) and other flatfish feed, gliding off into the distance when disturbed. These fish begin life with a shape similar to most common pelagic fish. Then, after a couple of months, one eye migrates around the head to lie on the same side of the body as the other. Progressively these developing fish then begin to swim in a horizontal orientation and move down to live on the sand.

The snakelocks anemone (*Anemonia viridis*), seen adhering to the blocks, often has striking green tentacles with purple tips. This animal has a trick up its sleeve, harbouring photosynthetic algae within its body from which it obtains additional food. A relative, the tube anemone (*Cerianthus lloydii)* has evolved a mucous tube home enabling it to live buried in the sand with only its feeding tentacles protruding. Dahlia anemones (*Urticina felina*), like the tube anemones, often appear to be emergent from the sand but invariably are attached to an

Little cuttlefish (*Sepiola atlantica*), swimming.

underlying rock of some kind.

At night the cuttlefish (*Sepiola atlantica*) emerges to hunt on the sand. In the day it is harder to spot, with only its tiny eyes poking out of the sand. Another molluscan predator, the lesser octopus (*Eledone cirrhosa*) behaves in a similar nocturnal way and is often seen prowling here at night, particularly later in the year.

Night diving reveals an alternative host of nocturnal creatures which hide secretively away during daylight hours. Spiny squat lobsters (*Galathea strigosa*) are abundant on the T-blocks but only squeeze their flattened bodies out from crevices at night. Similarly other crabs, such as the velvet swimming crab (*Necora puber*) and common shore crabs (*Carcinus maenas*), which often shelter by day in cryptic crevices are more evident by night. Hermit crabs (*Pagurus bernhardus*), on the other hand, are less cautious, the protection given them by their adopted shell home allowing them to be far more active by day.

Red mutant eyes shine mysteriously from the dark! This alien phenomenon is caused by the reflection of the diver's torch beam from crystals in the back of crustaceans' eyes, in a manner similar to cats' eyes on the road. Groups of prawns clambering by night over weed, or emerging from rocky crevices, create sparkling clusters of tiny luminous eye dots.

Many fish appear to doze at night, the ballan wrasse (*Labrus bergylta*) lying apparently drugged in sheltered recesses. Others, like the conger eel (*Conger conger*), emerge more often in the gloom and can be encountered on the sand amongst weed or hunting between the blocks.

There is a carnival of excitingly variable and easily accessible marine life in Port Erin Bay, as well as the less immediately obvious animals which can be found by investigating nooks and crannies during the day or by venturing into this beckoning realm by night.

Squat lobster (*Galathea strigosa*) at night, Port Erin Bay.

Bowes or Halfway Rocks

Bowes or Halfway Rocks close to low water as seen from the cliffs above.

DIVE SITE DETAILS

TIDAL streams at Bowes Rock flow north-easterly on the ebb and south-westerly, towards the Calf Sound, on the flood tide. During spring tides, currents may reach speeds in the order of two knots in gullies and off the point of the main rock itself. The best slack water at this site occurs two hours before high and low water, and currents, when perceptible, are strongest about one hour after each tide.

On the north-west, seaward, face of the rock (A) is an underwater cliff area.

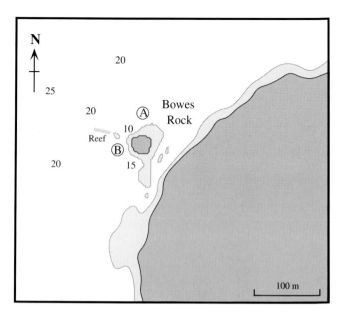

Beginning at around 5 m, this has its main base in around 12 m of water. The south-west flank of the rock also has an underwater cliff face, which descends from near the surface to around 10–15 m. This vertical face runs seawards to the gully (B), where it meets the north-west face and runs out westwards as a diminishing submarine reef to a depth of around 20 to 25 m, where it joins a sandy gravel plain.

One plan when diving this site is to drop divers close in on the north-west face (A) and for them to descend and swim south-west to the gully (B). From there they may proceed out along the reef, returning to the amphitheatre at the base of the south face of the rock, which also provides an interesting finalé and good reference for a controlled ascent.

GENERAL DESCRIPTION AND BIOLOGY

The underwater terrain at Bowes Rock is tremendously varied, with rock faces both exposed to and sheltered from the current and swells, giving rise to a fascinating mix of habitats which are home to a multitude of marine life. There are dense patches of species reminiscent of the higher current localities around the Calf even though currents here are not as severe.

The underwater cliff faces are often capped with kelp. Closer inspection of these forests reveals a multitude of intensely colourful small sponges, sea squirts, anemones and red algae packed in between the anchoring holdfasts, and growing on the kelp itself. No space is left vacant in this understorey world, with invertebrate life such as the jewel anemone (*Corynactis viridis*) and its relative *Sagartia elegans* vying for this valuable commodity. Living space within this environment is the ultimate prize, as suspended food for these creatures is brought past by the surging swells and currents.

Further down the cliffs, away from the seaweed, are more sponges, soft corals, anemones and hydroids. Although not as densely packed as at some of the other sites around the Calf, there are patches here of enormous richness and diversity, where seemingly every colour of the rainbow can be found in a square metre. Other areas on these rock faces are less intensely populated, possibly as a result of being more sheltered, but nevertheless house smatterings of interesting life.

Roaming this vertical landscape one can find the striking predatory blood star (*Henricia oculata*) and other relatives such as the cushion star (*Porania pulvillus*) and the common sea urchin (*Echinus esculentus*). All these animals owe their apparent strength of attachment to hundreds of tiny extensible tubefeet with sucker-like ends which can be thrown out and hauled on, like a web of grapples.

Amongst the boulder slopes at the base of the cliffs, congers (*Conger conger*) lurk, with their eerie, indifferent gaze. More commonly emerging after dark, they prey upon just about anything that moves, including relatively large fish and even octopus. Crustaceans may also fall foul of the conger, the mythically proportioned beast of many a diver's pub yarn. Inhabiting this labyrinth of nooks and crannies beneath the boulders are numerous kinds of crabs, the lobster (*Homarus gammarus*) and squat lobsters (*Galathea strigosa*). It is therefore not surprising that strings of lobster pots are nearly always seen at this site.

Particularly colourful examples of fish species are often encountered here including the scorpion fish (*Taurulus bubalis*), seen here sporting splashes of colours, seemingly without any sense of continuity or fashion! This is however a camouflage to suit their immediate habitat, be it green, red, purple or orange. All of these colours are possible and can be worn together! An equally colourful but more obvious resident is the male cuckoo wrasse (*Labrus mixtus*), found very occasionally with a white head patch when breeding. The cuckoo wrasse is easily lured to the practised diver, particularly by wiggling pale finger tips from a glove past its 'best-before' date!

Scorpion fish (*Taurulus bubalis*) in mottled camouflage.

Eventually, to the west, the bedrock and boulders give way to coarse sand and gravel where an array of different animals are found. A number of suspension feeders can be observed half buried in the sand: the nervous tube anemone (*Cerianthus lloydii*) which can rapidly retract its tentacles, often especially for photographers, and the sea cucumber (*Neopentadactyla mixta*) which, when studied closely, can be seen to suck its brushy mouth tentacles after collecting suspended food from the water. At night, one can find the predatory lesser octopus (*Eledone cirrhosa*) roaming these gravelly plains, blending into the background with its rapidly adaptable camouflage.

Due to its dense patchwork of marine life, relatively low currents and close proximity to Port Erin, Bowes Rock has become a popular and rewarding dive site.

The lesser octopus (*Eledone cirrhosa*), down on the gravel plains.

The Heifers

DIVE SITE DETAILS

THE Heifers, a rock close to the northern mouth of the sound was named, so the story goes, in reference to the fact that in times gone by cows were swum across the Calf Sound from the Isle of Man to Cow Harbour, to exploit grazing sites on the Calf. Tidal directions here are quite similar to those at Bowes Rock,

View towards the south-west showing Clet Aldrick, the Heifers and Thousla rock at low water.

flowing north-easterly on the ebb and south-westerly, towards the Calf Sound, on the flood. However, close proximity to the sound makes the

The dahlia anemone
(*Urticina felina*).

The blood star (*Henricia oculata*) amongst dead man's fingers (*Alcyonium digitatum*).

37

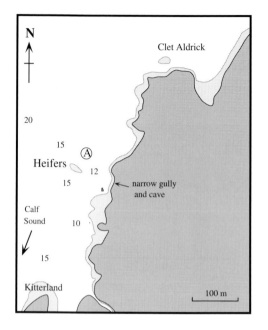

tidal flows here stronger and the development of localised eddies more likely. Slack water at this site occurs a little more than two hours before high and low water. Currents are strongest about an hour after the low tide and two hours after high tide.

The Heifers rock itself, or Im Leod in Manx, does not appear until about three hours before low water, when it begins to break the surface opposite a narrow gully and small cave on the shore. For easier location of the site, low- water slack is probably the best time to dive here.

Underwater, a bedrock and boulder slope with large gullies runs approximately east–west. Eventually this gives way to a sandy gravel plain at around 20 m. There are also a series of diminishing reefs westwards out to sea.

Divers can be dropped north-east of the emergent rock (A) and swim over interesting gullies towards it. From here they can progressively descend, around the rock, further to the south or west onto the gravel plain.

There are sometimes strong eddies present between the Heifers and Clet Aldrick to the north-east. If conditions are not entirely slack, care should be taken to ensure that divers are not unwittingly drawn into the powerful flows of the Calf Sound – particularly the shallow and often extremely fast-flowing Little Sound.

GENERAL DESCRIPTION AND BIOLOGY

The large gullies around this site produce interesting small scale cliffs. Below the kelp forest, in areas more exposed to the current, these cliffs are covered with colourful sponges such as the rock boring sponge (*Cliona celata)* and the elephant's ear sponge (*Pachymatisma johnstonia)*, anemones such as

Sagartia elegans, the plumose anemone (*Metridium senile*), *Actinothoe sphyrodeta,* the dahlia anemone (*Urticina felina*) and very occasionally the jewel anemone (*Corynactis viridis*). The colourful blood star (*Henricia oculata*) stands out amongst this variable background.

Many beautiful red algae occur in the shallower areas, particularly in spring and summer, amongst the holdfasts of the kelp forests or deeper among the anemones and sponges. These include the dark red bushy *Odonthalia dentata,* its name derived from the tooth-like margins of the fronds, and the smaller, more delicate (both in form and colour) *Plocamium cartilagineum,* which can give areas of rocks a soft meadowy appearance.

In cracks and crevices around the site velvet swimming crabs (*Necora puber*) can be seen with characteristic bold blue and black markings on their legs. A dense velvety covering of fine hairs on their shells gives them their name. Predatory crustaceans such as the lobster (*Homarus gammarus*) are also to be seen. Their threatening claws are used for crushing or cutting food, for defence, and for battling with others. Claws or legs lost in battle are gradually regrown in stages each time the unfortunate loser goes through its moult cycle. During this moulting process, the lobster casts off its old shell and grows rapidly to fill its next-sized suit of armour. It can take several moults over a few seasons to regenerate a completely lost limb to its appropriate size.

Down on the sandy gravel at the base of the rock are scavenging hermit crabs (*Pagurus bernhardus*) lumbering along with their clumsy adopted housing. Tubeworms, such as the sand mason worm (*Lanice conchilega*), protrude from the sand and gravel as thin granular straws. At their top is a precarious disarray of spindly branches formed from cemented sand grains. Waterborne food is trapped from the flow on these thin branches, as if through a coarse filter. The sticky tentacles of the worm inside the tube scrape particles of food from these constructions as well as from the adjacent sand.

The sand is home to the occasional great scallop (*Pecten maximus*), traditionally known in Manx as roagan. The lucky diver may also encounter flatfish or dogfish (*Scyliorhinus canicula*) here. Curiously, in the 1800s, the dogfish's rough skin was used as sandpaper for cleaning the decks of local fishing boats.

The Heifers is a very pleasant and leisurely dive around slack water. Care should be taken, however, when tides are running strongly in the Calf Sound.

The Wreck of the Clan McMaster

DIVE SITE DETAILS

This 6,563 ton cargo ship foundered in the Calf Sound during thick fog in 1923, carrying heavy machinery, sewing machines, cotton goods and coal. The wreck of the *Clan* caused a serious obstruction in the sound and it is reputed that she was later blown up to allow for the unhindered passage of other vessels. As a result of this drastic action only the remains of the aft half are worth diving.

The sternmost section now lies running north-east to south-west at the base of Thousla rock, parallel to, and on the northerly side of, the shallow Blind Sound between Thousla and the Calf of Man. The majority of the wreck is broken up at a maximum depth of around 18 m, although further sections are found in deeper water in the Calf Sound. Hull plating, as well as large sections of engine and boilers (A and B respectively), can still be easily recognised. A huge shaft, slightly raised off the bottom and running along most of the wreck, forms a distinct feature which can be used as a navigational reference.

Wreck of the *Clan McMaster* in 1923.

In the sound, slack water occurs approximately 1½ hours before high and low water, and it is at these times that dives on the *Clan McMaster* are easiest. However, because the wreck is in the shelter of Thousla, it is quite possible to dive here at

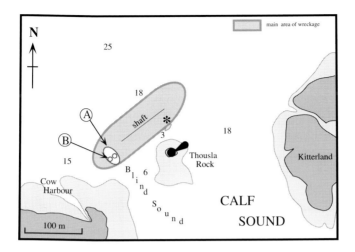

other times (e.g. in slight northward currents), depending on levels of confidence and experience.

Divers dropped just north of Thousla Rock (*) can descend the rocky slope to the wreck. Diver deployment can be tricky if not diving on slack, due to shallow reefs and currents in the sound. If the tide is running, one can easily get drawn up through the shallows of the Blind Sound past the boilers, and out of the shelter of Thousla Rock.

If a north to south drift is planned through the Calf Sound, some people favour starting their dive on the *Clan*. It is quite possible to explore the deeper part of this wreck before finning out round the north-east of Thousla into the current (See 'The Calf Sound Drift').

GENERAL DESCRIPTION AND BIOLOGY

Inquisitive ballan, corkwing and cuckoo wrasse (*Labrus bergylta*, *Crenilabrus melops* and *Labrus mixtus*) can be found here in the kelp-forested areas of the wreck. Many of these fish are fearless and will come close, expecting a payoff in the form of a free lunch, evidence of the popularity of this site.

Although a lot of the hull plating has a smattering of kelp on top, enquiry into the gloomy underhangs beneath the plates can reveal some explosively colourful patches of encrusting life, as well as scavenging crabs and lurking predatory fish such as the conger (*Conger conger*) and ling (*Molva molva*). It is also possible by day to find the more nocturnal lesser octopus (*Eledone cirrhosa*) squeezed, putty-like into hideaway crevices.

Exciting splashes of colour are displayed by the various forms of the plumose anemone (*Metridium senile*), especially on the underside of the huge propeller shaft, and by the anaemic hands of dead man's fingers (*Alcyonium digitatum*) which are also dotted around the wreck. Closer towards the Calf, in the shallower sections of this wreck, the looming boilers, engine structures and an upright hull section are to be found. Topped with kelp, and thick with hydroids and other encrusting animals, the once noisy bustle of the hugely powerful machinery seems dampened by a smothering blanket of life.

To the north, off the wreck in deeper water, the sea bed changes to sand and gravel areas which sport patches of quill-like hydroids (*Nemertesia antennina*) and brittle stars (*Ophiocomina nigra* and *Ophiothrix fragilis*). Moving around the north-east of Thousla Rock affords breathtaking views of the vivid encrusting life on the steep rock, if one doesn't fly past too quickly in the current!

This is an atmospheric, popular wreck and makes an excellent dive in an area that can provide interest in a relaxed, slack current environment. On the other hand the wreck can make a fascinating and novel start to an exhilarating drift dive through the Calf Sound.

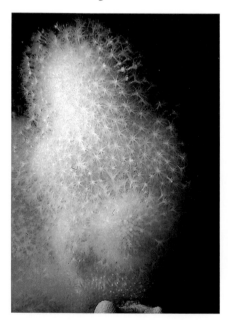

The orange form of the soft coral dead man's fingers (*Alcyonium digitatum*).

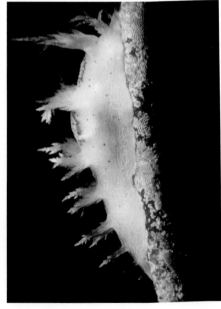

Sea-slug (*Dendronotus frondosus*), on kelp stipe.

The Calf Sound Drift

Aerial view of the Calf Sound including Kitterland (right) and Thousla Rock (centre).

DIVE SITE DETAILS

TIDAL streams through the Calf Sound can be extremely strong, making this a thrilling drift dive for the more experienced diver. Large volumes of water funnel through the Sound's relatively shallow and narrow confines on each tide and when the tidal flow is opposed by conflicting winds, enormous and daunting standing waves can develop.

Currents through the Calf Sound are at their strongest, often exceeding four knots, between one and two hours after high and low water. On the flood tide the waters in the sound run towards the south, and it is in this direction that the best drift dive is to be had. On the falling tide the direction of flow is northerly, towards the Port Erin side of the sound. Slack water occurs in the Calf Sound 1½–2 hours before high and low water.

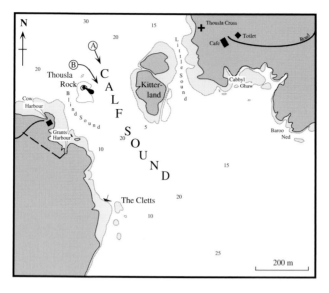

When drifting north to south through the sound it is best to drop divers halfway between Kitterland and Thousla Rock in the centre of the stream (A), thus avoiding the eddies and shallow kelpy areas on the periphery. Although these areas have plentiful and diverse patches of life, rushing through flailing kelp fronds at three or four knots is a good way to lose your equipment and sense of humour!

If the current is particularly strong, divers can be dropped northwards, 50 metres or so upstream, in order to allow time for their descent to the sea bed. An alternative dive plan is to start in the less boisterous water at the deeper part of the wreck of the *Clan Mc Master* (B), and to swim out into the main flow from here, being careful to avoid snagging surface marker buoy lines on the flank of Thousla Rock. The sound is well known for its wreckings, and the dismembered remains of these unfortunate vessels are occasionally encountered.

Divers are advised to stay well within no-stop times since ascents and stops for decompression in some of the more turbulent waters are not always within the full control of the diver. Buddy lines and surface marker buoys are recommended.

GENERAL DESCRIPTION AND BIOLOGY

Tides run with equal ferocity in both directions over the sea bed, which varies from coarse sand and gravel to boulders and bedrock. This creates a variety of habitats, and the fast flows provide an abundance of waterborne planktonic food upon which animals that can survive in the currents may thrive.

When drift diving here it is often next to impossible to appreciate anything specific through the swirling adrenalin haze other than the tremendous volume

Retracted plumose anemones (*Metridium senile*).

of life that prevails.

Great clusters of jewel anemones (*Corynactis viridis*) and dead man's fingers (*Alcyonium digitatum*) adorn the precipitous underwater flanks of Thousla Rock, fighting for space in this rich flow of abundant food. In the main channel plumose anemones (*Metridium senile*) form shimmering white drifts which knuckle down as the tide gets too strong, becoming retracted jellies on the rock. Intermittent sponge colonies look as if they have erupted from the bedrock, forming mounds and occasional thin yellow straw-like projections. Also evident is a lush hydroid turf and, as the sea bed slopes off into deeper water, bryozoans and hydroids form miniature coppices on the gravel. Crabs are occasionally seen, staggering tenaciously like mountaineers through a violent gale.

The Cletts comprise a series of rocks which are exposed at low water and are a common haul-out site for the resident grey seal (*Halichoerus grypus*) population. Consequently this area should be treated with respect. Sometimes seals will appear during dives in the sound. Glancing over your shoulder, you may catch a glimpse of them effortlessly shadowing you.

In the slower moving water, away from the central bottleneck of the sound, shoals of fish such as coley (*Pollachius virens*) are not uncommon and can make your ascent a spectacular swirling carousel conclusion to an exhilarating and beautiful dive.

Young male grey seal (*Halichoerus grypus*).

Gibdale – Creg Veanagh Drift

View along the north Calf from the south-west. Note the Stack in the foreground.

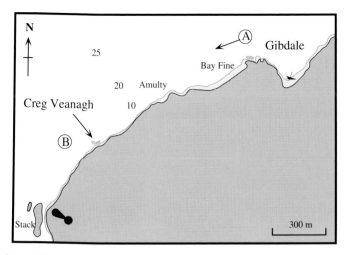

DIVE SITE DETAILS

THIS dive often provides a smooth drift of around one or two knots, and on neap tides it is suitable for the diver unaccustomed to currents. The tide runs towards the Stack, apart from during the period 1 ½ hours before high water to high water itself, when it slackens and then briefly flows towards the Calf Sound. The topography varies depending on the selected depth, with bedrock and boulder slopes close inshore leading eventually to coarse gravel and intermittent bedrock at around 20–25 m or so. Smoother drift conditions are found in this flatter area away from the more irregular, shallow rocky region. Care must be taken since the current picks up towards the west, becoming turbulent and quite ferocious at the Stack.

When diving here we usually deploy divers around point (A), to drift in the direction of the arrow, and pre-arrange that the boat cover should signal the divers via a surface marker buoy line to ascend once they arrive around point (B). This ensures that they *do not* drift by the Stack.

GENERAL DESCRIPTION AND BIOLOGY

The flat sea bed at around 20–25 m, with its coarse sand, cobbles and boulders, is an excellent place to find the feather star (*Antedon bifida*) and its brittle star relatives, the common brittle star and the black serpent star (*Ophiothrix fragilis* and *Ophiocomina nigra*). These animals use spines and the abundant tubefeet on their extended arms to catch food particles passing in the water, and are typical inhabitants of mid-energy sites. They are related to the starfish, urchins

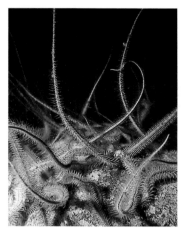

Mass of brittle stars.

and sea cucumbers also seen here, and are collectively referred to as echinoderms. The colourful, apparently placid, but extremely voracious predatory sunstars (*Crossaster papposus* and *Solaster endeca*) found here, like other starfish, turn their guts out to digest live prey items held firmly in their arms. Their prey is quite often other starfish! Common starfish (*Asterias rubens*) can be seen digging for shellfish in the sand. By pushing the sand aside with thousands of tiny tubefeet they gradually sink into a conical pit, mouth first, in a slow motion pursuit that can take hours. The vivid purple-red cushion star (*Porania pulvillus*), as well as being predatory, can gather particulate food by drawing water in using beating hair like cilia on its underside.

Occasionally one finds clusters of dead man's fingers (*Alcyonium digitatum*) and striking fields of the plumose anemone (*Metridium senile*) on boulders and outcrops of bedrock. The shallower areas, closer to the Calf, have more rocky surfaces and are clothed with these animals, growing as great glowing white mounds. Erratic patches of other anemone species punctuate the scenery and become increasingly lavish towards the current-swept Stack. Although thick with kelp, the shallower areas are good places to encounter seals and occasional impressive fish shoals.

A relaxing and effortless drift dive can be had in this area, gliding over patches and even fields of animals of many different kinds. Less experienced drift divers should however take great care with the looming proximity of the Stack and the increasingly turbulent currents that may be found there.

Grey seal (*Halichoerus grypus*) in the shallows.

The Stack

DIVE SITE DETAILS

THE Stack stands stark and proud at the north-west corner of the Calf of Man, with three lighthouses towering impressively on the cliffs above it. This 30 m, semi-crystalline basalt rock was regarded by the Norse as resembling a

Tide running on the Stack.

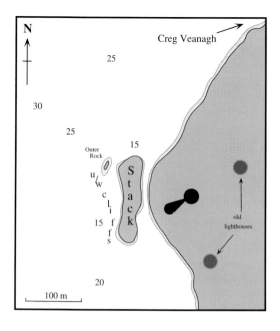

pile of hay. Hence they called it *Stakkr*, the word from which it derives its present name.

Currents here approach almost continually from the east, apart from a period from 1½ hours before high water to high water itself, during which slack water occurs for about forty minutes. After slack there is a short period of flow from the west, towards the sound. Slack conditions are quite variable, depending on the prevalence of neap or spring tides.

Cliffs and bedrock slopes descend to the south and west of the Stack to a coarse gravel bottom starting at around 20 m. Over the years the powerful tidal streams and current vortices have, in one or two places, shifted stones and eroded bedrock to form distinct, ominous circular craters about 10–15 m wide and up to a couple of metres deep.

Overhanging underwater cliffs are found on the outer face of the Stack, their bases at approximately 15 m or so.

GENERAL DESCRIPTION AND BIOLOGY

Like many of the dive sites around the Calf, the Stack is a very high-energy location, being regularly subjected to considerable current and wave action. The sweeping of great tides about the Stack makes diving it at slack water essential. As with many other high-energy sites, the density and variety of marine life present is certain to leave fond and indelible memories.

On the north-western flank of the Stack is a slightly overhanging, precipitous underwater cliff swamped in encrusting invertebrates. Pink, yellow and orange sponges, and a deluge of anemone species including *Actinothoe sphyrodeta*, *Sagartia elegans*, the plumose anemone (*Metridium senile*) and the jewel anemone (*Corynactis viridis*) are found crammed together. Topping these cliffs are thick kelp forests packed with profusions of red algae and encrusting life amongst the holdfasts. The cliff descends to around 15 m where sponges, particularly the elephant's ear (*Pachymatisma johnstonia*), seem to have erupted from the rock like cake-mix out of a baking tin. Others, such as *Polymastia boletiforme*, appear as a cluster of short orange-yellow straws protruding from the rock, while more flattened simpler forms crazily pave the seascape in a spectrum of colours.

Roaming and hunting in this exciting riot of life are many types of starfish. The blood star (*Henricia oculata*) not only occurs in a deep red form, but defies its name by also appearing in purple, yellow and striking combinations of these colours, which could well be testament to the individual's dietary history of mixed sponges, bryozoans or hydroids. Sunstars (*Crossaster papposus, Solaster endeca*), the common starfish (*Asterias rubens*) and the huge, knobbly spiny starfish (*Marthasterias glacialis*) are also to be found scattered around.

Away from the main rocky Stack, in deeper water (around 20 to 30 m) on the seaward side, there are patchy bedrock and boulder areas which provide a habitat for many crustacean inhabitants such as the velvet swimming crab (*Necora puber*), the common lobster (*Homarus gammarus*) and the edible crab (*Cancer pagurus*). Edible crabs can in theory grow to weigh several pounds and live up to eight years or more if left that long!

More plumose anemones (*Metridium senile*), sponges and feather stars (*Antedon bifida*) can be found in this area, particularly on the large, more stable boulders exposed to the current.

When conditions are suitable, seals can be seen hauled out on the tidally exposed rock just off the Stack. Cormorants (*Phalacrocorax carbo*), known to the Manx as jinney divers, and shags (*Phalacrocorax aristotalis*), are often seen here, and comical puffins (*Fratercula arctica*) can be seen on the cliffs either side of the Stack. All this above-water wildlife provides additional interest at a site already endowed with an impressive array of marine inhabitants.

A wealth of marine life, including the white anemone (*Actinothoe sphyrodeta*) and the yellow rock boring sponge (*Cliona celata*).

Emerging lobster (*Homarus gammarus*).

Chicken Rock

Tideswept Chicken Rock, from the south.

DIVE SITE DETAILS

SITUATED about one kilometre to the south-west of the Calf of Man, Chicken Rock towers 40 m from the sea bed, yet still remains a low, inconspicuous protuberance above the surface. The monumental 44 m lighthouse on this site, however, makes the Rock's location clearly visible from many miles away. Chicken Rock reputedly derives its name from the storm petrel (*Hydrobates pelagicus*) or Mother Carey's chicken.

Tidal streams here are amongst the most severe around the Isle of Man. Strong overfalls, up currents and eddies are commonplace and on a calm day at full flood the waters appear to boil. Even local pot fishermen find difficulty in accurately predicting tides here and our own experiences show that currents around the rock can switch on and off with unnerving rapidity.

Slack water on Chicken Rock occurs during the period from roughly two hours before low water to low water itself, and can last for as long as 1½ hours on a favourable neap tide. At high water the period of slack is much reduced and occurs during a period from about 1¼ hours before high water to high water itself. Both periods of slack vary depending on the weather and whether there are spring or neap tides. In some cases slack conditions are not at all apparent. When diving here it is best to plan to arrive on site about 30 minutes before expected slack, and to be prepared to wait until slack develops.

There are sheltered recessed areas on the eastern side (A) and the western side (B) of the rock, which provide semi-enclosed entry points. A bay (A) leads down to gullies and small amounts of wreckage at about 15 m. The rock then continues to shelve down reasonably quickly, giving way to more gently shelving bedrock and cobble slopes in a maximum depth of around 45 m. At 15–25 m on the western side there is a plateau which leads off as a gradual slope to depths in excess of 40 m. The southern end of the rock has a wonderful cliff which extends down to 25 m or so, where a few gullies may also be found. The northern flank of the rock is similarly steep.

Although potentially hostile, diving at Chicken Rock is extremely rewarding, offering perhaps the most exhilarating dive on the Island. However, attempting to dive here without previous experience of drift diving and strong currents is not to be advised.

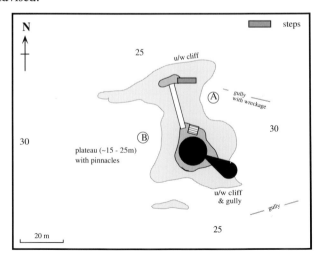

GENERAL DESCRIPTION AND BIOLOGY

As the sea plies tumultuously around this exposed rock, animals living in this current swept environment receive a deluge of suspended planktonic organisms from the passing water. This forms an abundant food source for the dazzling multitude of suspension-feeding animals which proliferate here.

The majority of these suspension feeders are invertebrates with particular adaptations to suit the location. They are characteristically anchored or cemented to the underlying bedrock, with tentacles or tiny projections to draw or seize their food from the passing water. Hydroids such as *Tubularia indivisa* are of this design, upholstering boulders and bedrock to give a soft overall appearance. Similarly, anemones such as the striking and aptly named jewel anemone (*Corynactis viridis*), form massive patchwork quilts of incredibly vivid and diverse colours. Elsewhere bryozoans form miniature tufty forests, and abundant sponge mounds appear to have oozed like toothpaste from the rock.

Of course, there is also a multitude of predators and scavengers to be found in this outer-space seascape. The edible crab (*Cancer pagurus*) is one of a number of conspicuous crustaceans here, roaming almost undisturbed in bulky armour. Velvet swimming crabs (*Necora puber*) with their acid red eyes, can be seen in abundance, scurrying in aggressive retreat.

A great myriad of nudibranchs, or sea slugs, graze their way through the invertebrate turf during the summer months, adding more startling colour detail to the overall picture. A recent survey found an amazing 56 such species around the Calf.

It is not uncommon when diving here to find shoaling fish such as the pollack (*Pollachius pollachius*), or callig in Manx. Occasionally divers become immersed in a great living cloud of these shimmering forms.

Chicken Rock is also a common haul out site for a few members of the resident Calf seal colony. Curious grey seals (*Halichoerus grypus*), sometimes seen basking at the surface, have been known to play with divers here or to escort them secretly through their dive like a bodyguard.

Chicken Rock, with its extremely diverse and plentiful marine life, offers a truly magnificent dive. We can only agree with the numerous experienced divers, underwater photographers and marine biologists who repeatedly acclaim it as one of the best sites in the British Isles.

A 'fortune' in jewel anemones (*Corynactis viridis*).

The edible crab (*Cancer pagurus*).

Caigher Point

Caigher Point (bottom left) and the Burroo (top right) from the west.

DIVE SITE DETAILS

CAIGHER Point is often beset by fierce currents. Slack water, if it occurs at all, can be quite limited, occurring approximately two hours before the tide. Tides run to the north on the ebb and to the south on the flood, although close inshore currents are complex. Large eddies form periodically, making accurate tidal predictions more difficult.

At the very point of Caigher (A) the sea bed plunges down towards the south in a steep bedrock slope to about 20 m. Further to the south, hummocks of bedrock rise in ridges up to 10 m high, with sandy gullies separating them.

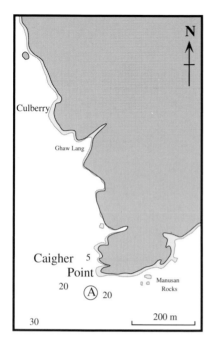

These hummocks diminish further southwards before giving rise eventually to a gently shelving stone gravel plain which begins at around 30 m and slopes off into the depths. West of the point, bedrock forms small towers and mounds in the shallower areas and similarly culminates in a stony gravel plain. East of the point, along the coastline, a boulder and bedrock slope extends southwards down to about 20 m, where more gravel and stony ground is interrupted by occasional bedrock outcrops.

Generally at this site, the closer one gets to the point itself the more bedrock is encountered and the more tidal effects are experienced when conditions are not slack.

GENERAL DESCRIPTION AND BIOLOGY

Bedrock and boulders form the majority of the substratum available to encrusting organisms here. Large gravelly plains run off to the south and west, hosting amazing expanses of feather stars, bryozoans and hydroids. The colonial tufts of bryozoans such as *Flustra foliacea* superficially resemble plants, but rather than having a herbaceous green colouration these colonies of planktonic particle feeders are beige. Close and careful examination reveals thousands of minuscule feeding tentacles protruding from the individual animals in the colony. Flat colonies of bryozoans (including *Electra pilosa* and *Membranipora membranacea*) can also be seen here in incredible numbers later in the year, smothering many algae in a white lacy coat.

As well as the familiar turfy hydroid *Tubularia indivisa*, there are little bunches of long grass-like hydroids such as *Nemertesia antennina* and *Kirchenpaueria pinnata*. All these colonies are constructed of many sticky-tentacled individuals.

Areas under and on the sides of large boulders to the south-east of the point exhibit further smatterings of fuzzy bryozoan species, but also hidden away in

The hydroid *Nemertesia antennina*, approximately 15 cm tall.

The sponge (*Hemimycale columella*) with the painted top shell (*Calliostoma zizyphinum*) in top left.

this topsy-turvy world can be found the more familiar clusters of dead man's fingers (*Alcyonium digitatum*) and anemones such as *Metridium senile*, *Actinothoe sphyrodeta* and *Sagartia elegans*. Deeper under these rocks, crabs and the lobster (*Homarus gammarus*) can be seen, and telltale excavations of shelly gravel from under boulders indicate their presence.

Bedrock mounds and protrusions are under acid attack from the yellow boring sponge (*Cliona celata*) which infiltrates the rocky sea bed and is amongst a host of sponges here which are found covering the bedrock. The peak abundance of sponges seems to occur directly off the point itself with many species including *Tethya aurantium* which looks like a shrivelled tennis ball, and *Hemimycale columella* which has the appearance of the surface of sliced bread. The upright, slimy and branched *Stelligera stuposa*, and the purse sponge (*Scypha ciliata*), are more unusual sponge species, the latter being generally more common in shallower water.

Caigher Point can be a rewarding though tricky place to dive on account of the complexity of the currents which can at times be found here.

The Puddle

The Puddle and the Burroo (bottom centre). Note South Harbour (right centre).

DIVE SITE DETAILS

THE Puddle, the largest bay around the Calf, constitutes in its entirety an area greater than most dive sites featured in this guide and consequently offers a wide variety of marine life.

On the whole, the majority of the Puddle is a gently sloping plain of coarse sand and occasional gravel down to approximately 25 m at the deepest. The shelly sand bottom begins at about 10–15 m at the margins of the bay, and is bordered by bedrock and boulder outcrops and slopes. In places the bedrock forms straight or stepped short cliffs extending to the surface.

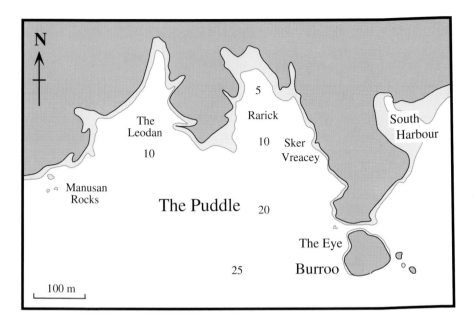

A blanket of mystery and rumour surrounds the possible existence of an ancient wreck somewhere in the bay, but supporting factual information is sparse. The story could well be true on account of the huge number of wrecks recorded around the Calf.

Currents in the Puddle are negligible, but become more apparent the closer one strays out of the bay towards the Burroo or Caigher. It is possible to venture out of the Puddle when the Burroo is slack, past the Eye over a series of ledges into the deeper water to the south-east, then reversing the journey to return and surface back in the sheltered confines of the Puddle. Even when the tide is running at the Burroo and Caigher Point, the Puddle offers a reasonably reliable refuge from the tidal streams, and can be a good site for the less experienced diver or anyone planning to avoid the current swept localities.

GENERAL DESCRIPTION AND BIOLOGY

The Puddle is unusual among the dive sites described in this book in that it is a comparatively calm, sandy environment, with a correspondingly dissimilar and contrasting array of marine life.

The coarse sandy gravel bottom in areas of this bay is home to many peculiar animals which partially protrude from the sea bed. Sand living tube anemones (*Cerianthus lloydii*), and sea cucumbers (*Neopentadactyla mixta*), have appendages which project into the water for feeding and breathing, the greater part of their bodies remaining hidden and protected below the sand. The sandy plains are far from deserted and beneath the surface are innumerable creatures actually living in the sand. The observant diver will spot small openings in the sea bed caused by shellfish and the heart urchin (*Echinocardium cordatum*) which are common here. On the sand surface are painted gobies and sand gobies (*Pomatoschistus pictus* and *P. minutus*), which are adapted to life on the bottom, unlike their relative the two spot goby (*Gobiusculus flavescens*), which is found in small shoals over weed-covered boulders.

A wide variety of patchy marine life can be found on the rocks and boulders around the bay. A notable increase in the density of rock-covering life, and a corresponding masking of bare bedrock, occurs as one swims towards the exposed headlands at the extremities of the bay. Devonshire cup corals (*Caryophyllia smithii*), the only true hard coral known to be found in the Irish Sea, can be found scattered about here. This is a solitary relative of the colonial cousins which dominate the tropical coral reefs of many a diver's dream. Another relative is the soft coral dead man's fingers (*Alcyonium digitatum*). This is a colonial organism, being composed of many individual polyps, each brandishing a set of eight tiny tentacles, and living in a communal soft structure. The individual polyps superficially resemble sea anemones.

The light bulb tunicate (*Clavelina lepadiformis*) and *Morchellium argus* are both sea squirts, although surprisingly different to look at. This is because the latter, like the dead man's fingers, is a colonial animal made up of individuals similar to the light bulbs of the related *Clavelina lepadiformis*.

Sponges such as *Cliona celata*, *Tethya spinosa* and *Polymastia boletiforme* are commonly found in the Puddle. *Polymastia boletiforme* and *Ciocalypta penicillus* are easily confused, both having curious straw-like protrusions called papillae, through which they expel water from which they have filtered food. *Ciocalypta penicillus* is, however, always found out on the sandy gravel, with its glassy straws poking above the sand surface.

On the whole the Puddle is a relaxed and varied environment in which to dive, favoured by some for its lack of troublesome tidal complexity, and by others for its marine life, much of which is different from that encountered elsewhere around the Calf.

The sea cucumber (*Neopentadactyla mixta*) right, and the tube anemone (*Cerianthus lloydii*), feeding.

Sea urchin (*Echinus esculentus*).

The Burroo

The Burroo from the east, showing the Eye through the rock.

DIVE SITE DETAILS

THE unusual name of this site, the Burroo, is derived from the Scandinavian word *borg*, meaning small round hill. Neither the name nor the bountiful and extremely striking marine life found here, are easily forgotten.

On the south of the Burroo the main cliff face continues underwater into short vertical drops and then becomes a bedrock and boulder slope (A). At around 15 m, this area provides a good, sheltered entry point. However, the Burroo, possibly once the site of some Nordic defences, is renowned as a favourite nesting place for many timid seabirds in the summer season, including guillemots (*Uria aalge*) and razorbills (*Alca torda*). Care should be taken not to disturb these birds.

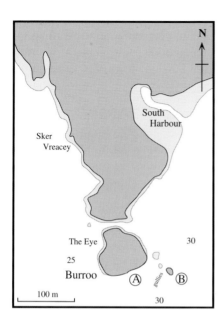

From the base of these cliffs, underwater a rocky incline with intermittent large bedrock mounds and boulders, runs off into the depths to the south and west.

The outer rock (B) makes a good entry point, with an underwater cliff falling to about 15–20 m. Just west of the outer rock, and in towards the main cliff, are a couple of large bowl-shaped gullies, one of which is referred to as 'the amphitheatre'. Trapped at the base of one of the small underwater faces in this area is a huge timber, no doubt from a ship, and possibly part of an old wreck rumoured to lie in the Puddle.

It is sensible to dive here at slack water, not least because there is deep water, around 50 m, to the immediate south and west. The time of slack water is somewhat variable, but starts about two hours before low water and can last for a little more than 1½ hours on a good neap tide. High water slack starts 2½–3 hours before the tide and lasts for a similar duration.

GENERAL DESCRIPTION AND BIOLOGY

This is a priceless dive site and many people's favourite around the Calf. In good visibility even the most seasoned diver is presented with an irresistible panorama of marine life. Even in poor visibility it is still easy to be stunned and engrossed by the sight of an enormous diversity of colourful smothering animals and plants crammed into the smallest of areas.

The Burroo has all the marvellous density of marine life associated with high current sites like Chicken Rock, but perhaps in a more jumbled and patchy arrangement. Consequently, no two dives here ever seem quite the same.

Descending the outer rock or the inner cliffs, the diver will find innumerable anemones including *Actinothoe sphyrodeta*, *Sagartia elegans* and the plumose anemone (*Metridium senile*). The latter often occurs in patches of miniature forms. Notably around the outer rock, jewel anemones (*Corynactis viridis*), bloated and gorged on the passing plankton, occur in every conceivable rainbow colour, and form small gregarious patches of dazzling design. These tiny animals, like other anemones, can multiply by splitting or cloning, producing identically coloured twin neighbours. Abutting one patch of copy-cats may be other patches of individuals of completely different colour forms, producing mind boggling mosaic patterns on the rocks.

There is an absolute deluge of sponges around the Burroo, including the architecturally impressive elephant's ear sponge (*Pachymatisma johnstonia*), which in places forms mountains the size of a suitcase. The rock boring sponge (*Cliona celata*) starts life inconspicuously inside limestone rocks and shell fragments. This species emerges to form the bold yellow masses present at many places around the Calf, but here one colony approaching three metres in diameter has been observed!

Wall to wall shagpile carpets of hydroids are everywhere, giving the rock escarpments and boulders a soft appearance. Away to the south and west, great plains of these hydroids (*Tubularia indivisa*) roll off into the depths. A clumsy diver will find that they are infested with pinkish, shrimp like caprellids, which get brushed from their homes, attaching and moving caterpillar-like on his dive suit. These weird, inconspicuous crustaceans are often superabundant in the hydroid turf, but frequently go unnoticed.

The outer rocks of the Burroo are used as a haul out site by a grey seal (*Halichoerus grypus*) colony and care should be taken to avoid disturbance. Seals, masters of underwater style and grace, are far bolder below the waves, and will sometimes appear on a dive, although often vanish once detected.

The Burroo is blessed with a good collection of fish species, in addition to its tremendous and truly spectacular invertebrate life. Wrasse species, for example, familiar from other locations in this guide are to be found here, as are occasional large shoals of pollack (*Pollachius pollachius*) or saithe (*Pollachius virens*).

Any description short of a laborious catalogue of species cannot do justice to the diversity of marine life at the Burroo. In fact, in the areas exposed to fast flow, it is something of a challenge to find a single square centimetre of bare bedrock, so abundant is the life here!

Orange plumose anemones (*Metridium senile*) and variably coloured *Sagartia elegans*.

Custard coloured jewel anemones (*Corynactis viridis*).

Kione Roauyr – Kione ny Halby Drift

South-east coast of the Calf leading to the Calf Sound and Spanish Head.

DIVE SITE DETAILS

BENEATH the towering cliffs of Kione Roauyr a boulder strewn bedrock slope descends to a gravel plain at around 20–25 m. This submarine profile continues largely unbroken to the headland north-east of South Harbour, Kione ny Halby.

When tidal conditions are suitable, an excellent gentle drift can be enjoyed,

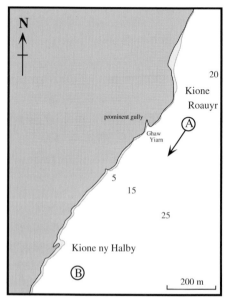

meandering at up to a couple of knots over rocky escarpments and between boulders the size of cars. Once on site a descent can be made near to Kione Roauyr (A) and boat cover can signal divers via their surface marker buoy lines once they get to around point (B). This enables divers to avoid drifting past the Burroo, where the current rapidly accelerates and can become more confused, forming impressive standing waves on the surface. Unwary divers could soon find themselves being drawn out towards Chicken Rock into water in excess of 40 m if they are allowed to proceed past this point.

On the ebb tide, water flows generally northwards through the Calf Sound and also diverges to move south-westerly along the coast of the Calf towards the Burroo. Curiously, on the flood the current runs similarly towards the Burroo but with water in the sound flowing south. Currents only run towards the sound along the south-east of the Calf from approximately one hour before until one hour after low water. Maximum current speeds can be encountered here between two and three hours after low water.

This dive can provide a relatively uniform and gentle drift dive for the diver less familiar with currents, although care should be taken as the Burroo is not recommended as a place where one should drift.

GENERAL DESCRIPTION AND BIOLOGY

The subsurface boulder slope at the foot of the deeply gouged cliff at Ghaw Yiarn is initially kelp forested. As one descends, the lush seaweed gradually thins to be replaced by undersea daisy meadows of the delicate white tentacled anemone (*Actinothoe sphyrodeta*) speckled on the upper surfaces of rocks and boulders. The petal-like tentacles of these animals are always white, although the central circular oral surface surrounded by them occurs in a variety of pastel shades of yellow, orange and white.

Gliding in the current over the huge boulders and outcrops of bedrock, festoons of the soft coral dead man's fingers (*Alcyonium digitatum*) can be seen protruding like the upheld hands of the implied long-perished mariners. In places the bedrock has a crazy paving appearance, purple-pink crusts of coralline algae blending harmoniously with areas of sponge and bryozoan. The broad trunks and bushy heads of the plumose anemone (*Metridium senile*) waft gently in the current although they recede defensively if disturbed, to become amorphous globular masses.

Underneath ledges and in the mysterious and gloomy recesses between boulders lurk lobsters (*Homarus gammarus*), conger (*Conger conger*) and occasionally ling (*Molva molva*). Conger, known in Manx as astan varrey, inhabit these and other European continental waters, until they reach a large size. They then stop feeding and migrate into deep water to spawn. The termination of feeding in these impressive fish is followed by the degeneration of most of their internal organs. The exception is the sex organs, which become massive for the last event of their lives.

Corkwing and ballan wrasse (*Crenilabrus melops* and *Labrus bergylta*) skittishly patrol the nearshore bouldery areas and often vanish should the intrusive beam of a torch probe too deeply into their privacy. Cuckoo wrasse (*Labrus mixtus*), on the other hand, are far more inquisitive, often shadowing divers, and on occasion will actually dare to peer into diving masks. The stunningly blue-coloured males, and smaller rose pink females (with three black marks on the base of their tails), are so distinct from each other that they were originally thought to be separate species.

Pollack (*Pollachius pollachius*), members of the cod family, are found here singly or in small shoals, often orientated to the flow and swimming gently. Down below the boulders, on the gravel, one occasionally finds the most common European shark, the dogfish (*Scyliorhinus canicula*). This hunter of shellfish and bottom-dwelling tiddlers is harmless to man and swims using an unmistakable sinusoidal S-shaped motion of the body, rather like a snake.

The Kione Roauyr – Kione ny Halby stretch of coast provides interesting terrain with beautiful scenic marine life. Exploration of recesses and crevices can yield further intrigue and enjoyment. One can drift safely and gently here, although the currents at and approaching the Burroo should be treated with great respect.

A forest of orange plumose anemones (*Metridium senile*).

Below. Male cuckoo wrasse (*Labrus mixtus*).

Spanish Head

The towering cliffs at Spanish Head.

DIVE SITE DETAILS

No British dive guide would be complete without the inclusion of the rumoured existence of a wreck of a Spanish galleon from the Armada fleet. South-east of the Calf Sound the awesome square cliff of Spanish Head is the reputed site of the demise of one such vessel in 1588, hence the name.

As shown on the tidal maps for the southern Isle of Man (page 14), the major current flow at Spanish Head is to the east on the flood and to the west on the ebb. Closer inshore, however, the current is often reversed as a result of

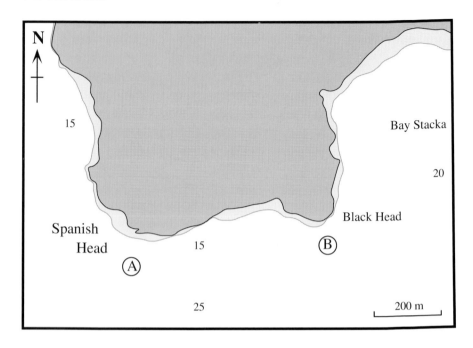

an apparent localised eddy. This can sometimes lead to confusion when predicting current direction here.

Tidal flows around the headland itself mean that this site can provide enjoyable drift dives. A good drift dive can be had by deploying divers beneath Spanish Head (A) or Black Head (B), depending on the direction of current flow.

Slack water is at approximately three hours before high and low water, although on spring tides it is of short duration. Beneath the sky-scraping cliffs of Spanish Head and Black Head, subtidal bedrock and huge boulders form a rugged slope down to between 20 and 25 m. Numerous small recesses and holes, with their inviting nooks and crannies, make this an attractive and interesting slack-water dive site. At slack water divers can be deployed anywhere along this section of coastline and descend the rock and boulder slope to their chosen depth.

It is important to note that currents in the sound can be very strong and divers may well choose to avoid drifting too far towards it on the ebb. When currents are strong, there are notable standing waves in this vicinity, particularly off Spanish Head itself.

General Description and Biology

Huge car-sized boulders parked at the base of the cliffs are covered with numerous colourful and interesting marine passengers. These boulders and the frequent holes, tunnels, nooks and crannies created by them, provide an abundant variety of habitats in which a contrasting array of life can be found. In good visibility the huge boulders add an aura to this site reminiscent of the scale of the cliffs above.

The nooks and crannies provide refuge for crabs, the lobster (*Homarus gammarus*) known as gimmagh in Manx, and a multitude of wrasse species common to many sites in this area. Some deeper holes are also home to the menacing looking conger (*Conger conger*), picked out by investigative torch light. Exploration into these holes can reveal miniature worlds, not apparent at first glance, where seasonally occasional sea slugs such as *Archidoris pseudoargus* or *Onchidoris luteocincta* can be seen. The former feeds on sponges, particularly the bread crumb sponge (*Halichondria panicea*).

Many sponges are found dotted around here, such as the large grey elephant's ear (*Pachymatisma johnstonia*) and the yellow coloured boring sponge (*Cliona celata*).

Small areas and patches of boulders exposed to the currents are densely covered with lush patches of the anemones *Actinothoe sphyrodeta* and *Sagartia elegans*. On a larger scale, areas of bedrock and boulders are sparsely peppered with these species, almost as if their scattered distribution were the result of a gentle fall of snowflakes. Jewel anemones (*Corynactis viridis*), with their characteristic vivid colours and the light-catching, club-like pinnate processes on the ends of their tentacles, can be found in occasional patches. These increase in abundance towards the west of this site, particularly in locations of greater current velocity.

Spanish Head makes a very interesting and fun dive site with many holes and features to explore. The use of torches is recommended to get the most from searching around the nooks and crannies. It can be a relatively easy dive here on neap tides, whether slack or drift diving. Currents can, however, be strong on spring tides.

Sagartia elegans

Actinothoe sphyrodeta with orange oral disc, on the yellow rock boring sponge (*Cliona celata*).

Sugar Loaf Caves

The Sugar Loaf cave system

DIVE SITE DETAILS

THE prospect of cave diving may conjure up threatening images to some divers. This site however, despite its name, offers clear surface diving throughout whilst still providing some of the intrigue and allure of subterranean systems.

The cave system consists of a voluminous hole extending into the cliff face (A) and a fissure in the rock which has created the Passageway running through the cliff to the sea stack. With a maximum depth of around 15 m, the deepest area is to be found at the end of the Passageway nearest the Sugar Loaf

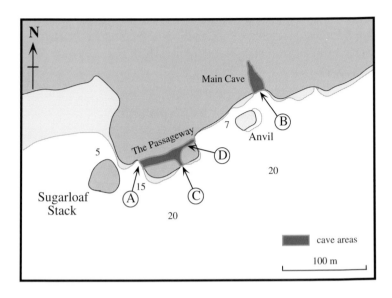

Stack. Behind the Anvil, a channel runs concurrent with the Passageway to the entrance of the Main Cave (B), allowing the whole area to be explored in one dive. There is also a side entrance to the Passageway (C) which opens to the south, creating tremendous atmospheric lighting on sunny days. Parts of the Sugar Loaf system can be quite shallow, and many people prefer not to dive here at low water to avoid possible sea swells associated with shallow water and confined spaces. Torches are essential, although during the day it is never completely dark in the caves.

Currents here sometimes cause a problem. A restriction in one part of the Passageway (D), only a little more than two bodies wide, occasionally causes an increase in current which can hinder divers. In such instances it is as well to deploy divers so that they go with any localised flow, rather than labour against it. They can be deployed at one end of the system and collected at the other. Dives carried out around high water generally do not encounter such problems.

GENERAL DESCRIPTION AND BIOLOGY

This is a truly enchanted and atmospheric place to dive. The tall overhanging sides, baronial halls and underwater passages could well have come from the pages of Tolkien's fantasy *The Lord of the Rings* – he must have been a diver!

Outside the caves, above the cliffs, the jet black chough (*Pyrrhocorax*

pyrrhocorax), with its distinctive call, swirls mysteriously amongst a myriad of seabirds including fulmars (*Fulmarus glacialis*), guillemots (*Uria aalge*) and razorbills (*Alca torda*) which nest here.

There is an endless supply of animal life hidden in the recesses here, including a few sponge species, such as *Cliona celata*, *Polymastia boletiforme* and *Dercitus bucklandi*. The latter is a black species that has a curious habit of bridging crevices. The elephant's ear sponge (*Pachymatisma johnstonia*) is also plastered around the place, occurring in some unusual anaemic looking growth forms in the caves.

Sumptuous feasts of the tangy red baked bean tunicates (*Dendrodoa grossularia*) dominate huge areas inside the Main Cave, and examination of these reveals that each has two openings, through which water is pumped in and out for food and respiration. The observant diver will notice a stringy, white mesh-like sponge called *Clathrina coriacea* draped between these tunicates.

Squat lobsters (*Galathea strigosa*) can be found in ranks along some of the cracks around the cave system, and the occasional velvet swimming crab (*Necora puber*) and common shore crab (*Carcinus maenas*) hide in the crevices. The hard armoured shell of these crustaceans is their skeleton, and can represent up to 40 per cent of the weight of the animal.

The channel between the Main Cave and the Passageway has an overhanging face on the landward side. Here a small fluffy coat of bryozoans can be found, along with numerous other hide-away species including several sponges and a small pink and quite rare close relative of the dead man's finger called *Parerythropodium coralloides*. Some of these animals are widespread in the Passageway as well, and are joined by a thick meadow of hydroids such as *Tubularia indivisa*, whose stems arise from the mass of other rock encrusting organisms. Anemone species are also found here including *Actinothoe sphyrodeta* and variously coloured dahlia anemones (*Urticina felina*). Look out for the rare vivid blue form of beadlet anemone (*Actinia* sp.) at the back of the main cave.

At the right time of year, interesting algal species can be found in the channel. In shallower areas the grockle kelp (*Saccorhiza polyschides*), with its warty base, is seen, and the strap-like dabberlocks kelp (*Alaria esculenta*) can be seen in plots on the more wave-exposed rocks around the Main Cave. The boulders and cobbles in the floor and entrance to the Main Cave are rarely colonised, probably because they are fairly mobile, testament to the ferocity of swells which must have played a strong part in the cave's formation.

A feast of baked bean tunicates (*Dendrodoa grossularia*).

Large areas of the stable rock surface are painted with purple, encrusting coralline algae. The branching coral weed (*Corallina officinalis*) is another coralline alga with a chalky skeleton. Abundant in the shallows, this species is constructed of strings of bead like structures which make up the whole tuft.

Common examples of wrasse, characterised by their thick lips, single long dorsal fin and habit of manoeuvring with their pectoral fins, include corkwing, ballan, goldsinny and cuckoo wrasse (*Crenilabrus melops, Labrus bergylta, Ctenolabrus rupestris* and *Labrus mixtus*). Ballan wrasse crush food items such as shellfish with a set of teeth in their throats known as the ballan cross on account of it's shape. Local sailors used to wear this bone as a charm against being lost at sea.

The Yarrell's and tompot blenny (*Chirolophis ascanii* and *Parablennius gattorugine*), with their amusing and distinctive head gear and the butterfish (*Pholis gunnellus*) can all be seen, often with their heads poking out of holes or crevices, and occasionally out and about on the Passageway walls. Small two spot gobies (*Gobiusculus flavescens*) are also evident in the kelpy shallows.

The Sugar Loaf Caves provide a great variety of fascinating and resplendent marine life far in excess of the examples mentioned above. All this life is framed in the most magical setting and in moderate depth, providing a purely inspirational and leisurely dive.

Two spot goby (*Gobiusculus flavescens*).

Port St Mary Ledges Drift Dive

Port St Mary Ledges

DIVE SITE DETAILS

THE rock strata in this area create broad step-like features or ledges, hence the name. The nature of the dive around these ledges is dependent on the speed of the drift and the entry point, and an element of good fortune is needed to see the most exciting and attractive areas. At around 20 m the sea bed is relatively level, with outcrops of bedrock amongst areas of rippled sand and gravel. These changes in the sea bed mean that the marine life occurs in patches, with the highest densities occurring on the exposed areas of bedrock.

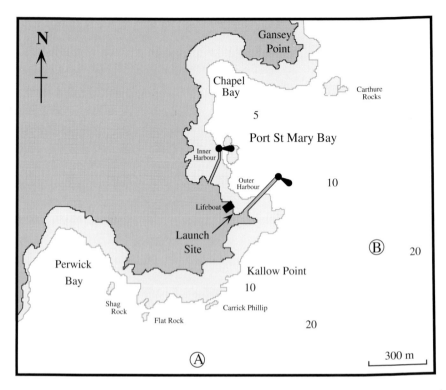

Shallower dives will tend to take the diver over more rock and kelp-covered areas. The deeper dive will consist of greater areas of sand and gravel. Ideally, to fully appreciate this site, the diver requires a drift at around 20 m, leading over the patchy profusions of life on the areas of bedrock, as well as over the expanses of contrasting life on coarse sand and gravel.

The flood tide runs to the north-east and the ebb to the south-west. Slack water occurs here approximately three hours before the tide. When the tide runs to the north-east a good diver drop off point is around point (A), point (B) being better on the reverse tide. It is worth noting that this site can be used as a useful introduction to drift diving for the less experienced diver.

GENERAL DESCRIPTION AND BIOLOGY

Patches of bedrock protruding from the gravel plain are often covered with sponges, commonly the elephant's ear sponge (*Pachymatisma johnstonia*), the rock boring sponge (*Cliona celata*) and the soft coral dead man's fingers (*Alcyonium digitatum*).

Occasionally one may be lucky enough to see the now rare crayfish (*Palinurus elephas*) in a hole, or maybe even wandering over the gravel plains. The fine delicate claws of this animal are used to manipulate food and not for defence or crushing, as are the larger claws of its cousin, the lobster (*Homarus gammarus*).

The intermittent gravel plains between the bedrock outcrops are not devoid of life as some may expect. The anemone *Cerianthus lloydii* and the colourful dahlia anemone (*Urticina felina*) can be seen here. The great scallop (*Pecten maximus*) also survives in these areas of gravel between the bedrock ledges, in refuge from dredging.

Gurnards can be seen fiddling in the sand with the first three fin rays of their pectoral fins. These are thickened and separated from the fin, resembling small fingers, and are used to feel and taste in the sand for food. Gurnards grunt at one another using vibrations of the swim bladder, and this startling sound can sometimes be heard underwater. Dragonets (*Callionymus lyra*), with neon blue markings on the males, can sometimes be seen roaming the gravel areas. Plaice (*Pleuronectes platessa*) and other flatfish can also be found here on the more sandy areas. They are adept at nipping off the tubular siphons of shellfish which poke from the sand and can be long-lived, capable of surviving to 30 years old.

Port St Mary Ledges can be an attractive and gentle drift dive particularly in good visibility, and can offer a pleasant and varied introduction to drift diving.

The elephants ear sponge (*Pachymatisma johnstonia*).

The feather star (*Antedon bifida*).

Glossary

Buddy line	a safety line employed to prevent dive buddies from becoming separated.
Carnivore	a meat eater.
Cilia	minute hair-like structures, often involved in the generation of water currents.
Clone	an individual derived from another by cloning.
Cloning	a process by which some organisms may reproduce, resulting in offspring identical to the parent.
Coralline	including a chalky supportive structure.
Decompression	the release from body tissues of excess gasses accumulated whilst under pressure during a dive.
Detritovore	a consumer of detritus.
Detritus	dead organic remains.
Dive time	the time elapsed from leaving the surface at the beginning of a dive to arrival at a specific depth on the ascent to the surface.
Dorsal fin	central fin on the back of a fish.
Drift dive	a dive during which one deliberately moves along with the prevailing current.
Eddies	localised cyclical currents which often develop in the lee of stationary objects.
Ebb tide	a falling tide.
Encrusting	growing as a surface layer.
Environment	an object or organism's natural surroundings.
Fetch	the distance across water over which wind acts to create waves.

Fin ray   a supporting rod-like structure within fish fins.

Flood tide   a rising tide.

Food chain   a representation of a series of organisms dependent on one another for food.

Food web   a diagrammatic representation of feeding interactions between organisms.

Habitat   an environment with characteristic physical and biological conditions.

Haul out site   a place where seals regularly come out of the sea.

Herbivore   a plant eater.

High energy environment

an area that receives much water movement, be it in the form of wave action or exposure to current.

Holdfast   the attachment part of a seaweed, securing it to whatever it is growing on.

Indigenous   naturally occurring.

Invertebrate   an animal without a backbone.

Knot   a measure of speed: one nautical mile per hour.

Larval phase   the free-living stage of an organisms life, between the egg hatching and the adult form.

Microcosm   a miniature imitation of a typically greater whole.

Neap tides   tides at half moon, with least height difference between high and low water.

Nocturnal   active after dark.

No-stop time   the maximum dive time allowed at a particular depth before incurring a necessary decompression stop.

Organism   a living individual.

Overfalls   turbulence caused by the passage of flowing water over an irregularity of the sea bed. Often produces associated surface disturbances.

Pectoral fin   one of a pair of fins often located to the rear of the fish's gill openings.

Pelagic   free living in the water column.

Photosynthesis   the process by which light energy from the sun is harnessed by plants to produce food, in the form of sugars.

Photosynthetic   capable of photosynthesis.

Phytoplankton	small, often single-celled, plants floating freely in the sea.
Pinnate	club ended.
Plankton	free-floating animals and plants in the water column.
Planktonic	floating freely in water.
Planktivore	a consumer of plankton.
Plankton grazers	systematic consumers of plankton.
Polyp	an individual invertebrate animal often within a colony.
Predator	an active hunter of live animal prey for food.
Recompression	treatment for diving injuries including the bends, in a pressurised chamber.
Respiration	absorption of oxygen and emission of carbon dioxide. Breathing
Siphons	tubular structures which facilitate the passage of seawater into and out of an organism. Often used for ventilation or feeding.
Slack water	the period during which there is little or no tidal water flow.
Species	a reproductively isolated group of interbreeding organisms which is usually distinguishable from other species by physical characteristics.
Spring tide	tides at full and new moon, with the greatest height range between high and low water.
Substratum	the underlying surface for attachment.
Surface marker buoy	a buoy on the surface that is attached to, and marks the position of, divers.
Suspension feeder	an animal that feeds on particulate matter suspended in the water.
Swim bladder	gas-filled bladder used for buoyancy control in fish.
Terrestrial	on or of the land.
Tidal stream	a current attributable to tidal activity.
Topography	the physical relief of a surface.
Trophic level	position occupied by an organism within the food chain.
Tube feet	protrudable, mobile hydraulic structures used for locomotion, e.g. in starfish or sea urchins.
Understorey	the level beneath the main seaweed canopy.

Bibliography

Ackers, R. G., Moss, D., Picton, B. & Stone, S. M. K. *Sponges of the British Isles (Sponge IV)*. Marine Conservation Society, Ross-on-Wye, 1985.

Bagenal, T. B. *The Observers Book of Sea Fishes*. Frederick Warne, London, 1979.

Barnes, R. D. *Invertebrate Zoology*. 4th ed. Holt-Saunders, Tokyo, 1980.

Barnes, R. S. K. & Hughes, R. N. *An Introduction to Marine Ecology*. Blackwell Scientific Publications, Oxford, 1986.

Barrett, J. & Yonge, C. M. *Collins Pocket Guide to the Sea Shore*. 14th ed. Collins, London, 1985.

Boucet, P., Darigal, F. & Huyghens, C. *Living Sea Shells*. Blandford Press, Poole, 1979.

Boyle, P. R. *Molluscs and Man*. Edward Arnold, London, 1981.

Cambell, A. C. *The Seashore and Shallow Seas of Britain and Europe*. Country Life. 8th ed. Country Life Books, 1985.

Crothers, J. & Crothers, M. *A Key to the Crabs and Crab-like animals of British Inshore Waters*. The Richmond Publishing Co., Richmond, 1988.

Dipper, F. *British Sea Fishes*. Underwater World Publications, London, 1987.

Dipper, F. & Powell, A. *Field Guide to the Water Life of Britain*. Readers Digest Association, London1984.

Erwin, D. & Picton, B. *Guide to Inshore Marine Life*. Immel Publishing, London, 1987.

Fincham, A. A. *Basic Marine Biology*. Cambridge University Press, Cambridge, 1984.

Furness, R. W. & Monaghan, P. *Seabird Ecology*. Blackie & Son, London, 1987.

Garrad, L. S. *The Naturalist in the Isle of Man*. David & Charles Ltd, Newton Abbot, Devon, 1972.

Hawkins, S. J. & Jones, H. D. *Rocky Shores*. Immel Publishing, London, 1992.

Hayward, P. J. *Animals on Seaweeds*. The Richmond Publishing Co., Richmond, 1988.

Hayward, P. J. & Ryland, J. S., ed. *The Marine Fauna of the British Isles and North West Europe*. 2 vols. Clarendon Press, Oxford, 1990.

Hildebrand, M. *Analysis of Vertebrate Structure*. John Wiley & Sons, New York, 1982.

Howson, C. M., ed. *Directory of the British Marine Fauna and Flora*. Marine Conservation Society, Ross-on-Wye, 1987.

Jangoux, M., 'Food and Feeding mechanisms: Asteroidea.' In *Echinoderm Nutrition*. Jangoux, M. & Lawrence, J.M. eds. A.A. Balkena, Rotterdam, 1982.

Laverack, M. S. & Dando, J. *Lecture Notes on Invertebrate Zoology*. Blackwell Scientific Publications, Oxford, 1974.

Lewis, R., *The Calf of Man and its Marine Life*, 1991.

Lockington Marshall, W., *The Calf of Man*. Shearwater Press, Isle of Man, 1985.

Manx Heritage Foundation., *Manx Sea Fishing*. Manx Heritage Foundation in co-operation with the Manx Museum and National Trust, Isle of Man, 1991.

McMillan, N. F. *The Observer's Book of Seashells of the British Isles*. Frederick Warne, London, 1977.

McNeill-Alexander, R. *The Chordates*. Cambridge University Press, Cambridge, 1979.

Morrow, C. C., Picton B. E. & Bishop, J. D. D. *A Sublittoral Survey of the Calf of Man*. Calf Marine Trust Publications, Isle of Man, 1993.

Newell, G. E. & Newell, R. C. *Marine Plankton*. Hutchinson Educational Limited, London, 1973.

Page, Rev. G. A. *Kitterland Disaster*. M.A. Quiggin, Douglas, 1853.

Vogel, S. *Life in Moving Fluids, the Physical Biology of Flow*. Princetown University Press, Princetown, New Jersey, 1983.

Webb, J. E., Wallwork, J. A. & Elgood, J. H. *Guide to Invertebrate Animals.* 2nd ed. Macmillan Press, London, 1981

West, M. '29 perished when gunpowder exploded.' *Isle of Man Examiner,* 18th August 1992, p. 24.

Young, J. Z. *The Life of Vertebrates.* 3rd ed. Oxford University Press, Oxford, 1985.

MAPS

Department of Local Government and the Environment, 1988.
Isle of Man Public Rights of way and Outdoor Leisure Map. Department of Highways Ports and Properties, Isle of Man.

Sheet L(D3) 2094. Admiralty Chart

Sheet SC 16NE I.O.M.   Ordnance Survey

Sheet SC 16SE I.O.M.   Ordnance Survey

Sheet SC 17SE I.O.M.   Ordnance Survey

Sheet SC 26NW I.O.M. Ordnance Survey   1869.

ISLE OF MAN (RUSHEN SHEADING) Sheet XV .15.   1869.

ISLE OF MAN (RUSHEN SHEADING) Sheet XVIII .2. 1869.

ISLE OF MAN (RUSHEN SHEADING) Sheet XVIII .3. 1869.

ISLE OF MAN (RUSHEN SHEADING) Sheet XVIII .4. 1986.
Isle of Man Series M 726, Sheet 95. 3 - GSGS ed.   Ordnance Survey: Southampton.

Index

The Authors

Bill Sanderson, Bruce McGregor and Andrew Brierley are highly qualified, experienced divers and trained marine biologists with an enthusiasm for promoting awareness and conservation within a sport which has become an integral part of their lives. They have a mutual desire to share with others the delights of diving the special piece of Manx heritage which is the Calf of Man, an area repeatedly recognised as providing some of the best scenic diving in the British Isles, and one which has been shown in recent surveys to exhibit a particularly high species diversity.

Bill Sanderson has been a devoted diver for the past eight years, having dived extensively around the UK and the Isle of Man, and also on expeditions to various locations in the Caribbean. He has also become an obsessive underwater photographer, helping to establish and co-organise the annual Manx National 'Splash In'.

Bruce McGregor has six years intense diving and marine survey experience around the Calf of Man alone. A diver for over 13 years, he has participated in a large-scale biological diving expedition to the Azores, as well as directing club diving and international expeditions as Diving Officer of his branch.

Andrew Brierley has been diving for over nine years. As well as having extensive experience of both scientific and pleasure diving in the Irish Sea, he has helped organise and participated in a conservation-orientated diving expedition to the Galápagos Islands, and more recently has been involved in scientific surveys on Australia's Great Barrier Reef.

The authors have worked closely together in many ways: as marine research scientists; as diving instructors; organising local and expedition diving ventures; as underwater salvers; and now in the compilation of this book. They hope that some of their passion and regard for the marine world will rub off on the reader and motivate them to discover, enjoy and conserve the natural beauties which Manx diving has to offer.